A DEFE[
CALVINISM

C. H. Spurgeon

THE BANNER OF TRUTH TRUST

THE BANNER OF TRUTH TRUST
3 Murrayfield Road, Edinburgh EH12 6EL, UK
PO Box 621, Carlisle, PA 17013, USA

*

© The Banner of Truth Trust 2008

ISBN-13: 978 0 85151 973 9

*

Typeset in 12/16 pt Adobe Garamond Pro
at the Banner of Truth Trust

Printed in the USA by
Versa Press, Inc.,
East Peoria, IL

The content of this booklet is taken from Chapter 13 of
The Early Years, Volume 1 of *C. H. Spurgeon's Autobiography*
(London: Banner of Truth, 1962,
reprinted often).

We only use the term 'Calvinism' for shortness. That doctrine which is called 'Calvinism' did not spring from Calvin; we believe that it sprang from the great founder of all truth. Perhaps Calvin himself derived it mainly from the writings of Augustine. Augustine obtained his views, without doubt, through the Spirit of God, from the diligent study of the writings of Paul, and Paul received them of the Holy Ghost, from Jesus Christ, the great founder of the Christian dispensation. We use the term then, not because we impute any extraordinary importance to Calvin's having taught these doctrines. We would be just as willing to call them by any other name, if we could find one which would be better understood, and which on the whole would be as consistent with fact. – C. H. S.

The old truth that Calvin preached, that Augustine preached, that Paul preached, is the truth that I must preach today, or else be false to my conscience and my God. I cannot shape the truth; I know of no such thing as paring off the rough edges of a doctrine. John Knox's gospel is my gospel. That which thundered through Scotland must thunder through England again. – C. H. S.

THE IMPORTANCE OF SOUND TEACHING

It is a great thing to begin the Christian life by believing good solid doctrine. Some people have received twenty different 'gospels' in as many years; how many more they will accept before they get to their journey's end, it would be difficult to predict. I thank God that he early taught me *the* gospel, and I have been so perfectly satisfied with it, that I do not want to know any other. Constant change of creed is sure loss. If a tree has to be taken up two or three times a year, you will not need to build a very large loft in which to store the apples. When people are always shifting their doctrinal principles, they are not likely to bring forth much fruit to the glory of God. It is good for young believers to begin with a firm hold upon those great fundamental doctrines which the Lord has taught in his Word. Why, if I believed what some preach about the temporary, trumpery salvation which only lasts for a time, I would scarcely be at all grateful for it; but when I know that those whom God saves he saves with an everlasting salvation, when I know that he gives to them an everlasting righteousness, when I know that he settles them on an everlasting foundation of everlasting love, and that he will bring them to his everlasting kingdom, oh, then I do wonder, and I am astonished that such a blessing as this should ever have been given to me!

Pause, my soul! adore, and wonder!
  Ask, 'Oh, why such love to me?'
Grace hath put me in the number
  Of the Saviour's family:
      Hallelujah!
  Thanks, eternal thanks, to Thee!

THANKFULNESS FOR GRACE

I suppose there are some persons whose minds naturally incline towards the doctrine of free-will. I can only say that mine inclines as naturally towards the doctrines of sovereign grace. Sometimes, when I see some of the worst characters in the street, I feel as if my heart must burst forth in tears of gratitude that God has never let me act as they have done! I have thought, if God had left me alone, and had not touched me by his grace, what a great sinner I should have been! I should have run to the utmost lengths of sin, dived into the very depths of evil, nor should I have stopped at any vice or folly, if God had not restrained me. I feel that I should have been a very king of sinners, if God had let me alone. I cannot understand the reason why I am saved, except upon the ground that God would have it so. I cannot, if I look ever so earnestly, discover any kind of reason in myself why I should be a partaker of Divine grace. If I am not at this moment without Christ, it is only because Christ Jesus would have his will with me, and that will was that I should be with him where he is, and should share his glory. I can put the crown nowhere but upon the head of him whose mighty grace has saved me from going down into the pit. Looking back on my past life, I can see that the dawning of it all was of God; of God effectively. I took no torch with which to light the sun, but the sun enlightened me. I did not commence my spiritual life, I rather kicked, and struggled against the things of the Spirit: when he drew me, for a time I did not run after him: there was a natural hatred in my soul of everything holy and good. Wooings were lost upon me – warnings were cast to the wind – thunders were despised; and as for the whispers of his love, they were rejected as being less than nothing and vanity. But, sure I am, I can say now, speaking on behalf of myself, 'He only is my salvation.' It was he who turned my heart, and brought me down on my knees before him. I can in very deed, say with Doddridge and Toplady:

> Grace taught my soul to pray,
> And made my eyes o'erflow;

and coming to this moment, I can add –

> 'Tis grace *has* kept me to this day,
> And will not let me go.

HOW I CAME TO BE A CHRISTIAN

Well can I remember the manner in which I learned the doctrines of grace in a single instant. Born, as all of us are by nature, an Arminian, I still believed the old things I had heard continually from the pulpit, and did not see the grace of God. When I was coming to Christ, I thought I was doing it all myself, and though I sought the Lord earnestly, I had no idea the Lord was seeking me. I do not think the young convert is at first aware of this. I can recall the very day and hour when first I received those truths in my own soul – when they were, as John Bunyan says, burnt into my heart as with a hot iron, and I can recollect how I felt that I had grown on a sudden from a babe into a man – that I had made progress in scriptural knowledge, through having found, once for all, the clue to the truth of God. One week-night, when I was sitting in the house of God, I was not thinking much about the preacher's sermon, for I did not believe it. The thought struck me, *'How did you come to be a Christian?'* I sought the Lord. *'But how did you come to seek the Lord?'* The truth flashed across my mind in a moment – I should not have sought him unless there had been some previous influence in my mind to make me seek him. I prayed, thought I, but then I asked myself, *'How came I to pray?'* I was induced to pray by reading the Scriptures. *'How came I to read the Scriptures?'* I did read them, but what led me to do so? Then, in a moment, I saw that God was at the bottom of it all, and that he was the Author of my faith, and so the whole doctrine of grace opened up to me, and from that doctrine I have not departed to this day, and I desire to make this my constant confession, 'I ascribe my change wholly to God.'

I once attended a service where the text happened to be, *'He* shall choose our inheritance for us'; and the good man who occupied the pulpit was more than a little of an Arminian. Therefore, when he commenced, he said, 'This passage refers entirely to our temporal inheritance, it has nothing whatever to do with our everlasting destiny, for', said he, 'we do not want Christ to choose for us in the matter of heaven or hell. It is so plain and easy, that every man who has a grain of common sense will choose heaven, and any person would know better than to choose hell. We have no need of any superior intelligence, or any greater Being, to choose heaven or hell for us. It is left to our own free-will, and we have enough wisdom given us, sufficiently correct means to judge for ourselves', and therefore, as he very logically inferred, there was no necessity for Jesus Christ, or anyone, to make a choice for us. We could choose the inheritance for ourselves without any assistance. 'Ah!' I thought, 'but, my good brother, it may be very true that we *could,* but I think we should want something more than common sense before we *should* choose aright.'

GOD'S OVER-RULING PROVIDENCE

First, let me ask, must we not all of us admit an over-ruling Providence, and the appointment of Jehovah's hand, as to the means whereby we came into this world? Those men who think that, afterwards, we are left to our own free-will to choose this one or the other to direct our steps, must admit that our entrance into the world was not of our own will, but that God had then to choose for us. What circumstances were those in our power which led us to elect certain persons to be our parents? Had we anything to do with it? Did not God himself appoint our parents, native place, and friends? Could he not have caused me to be born with the skin of the Hottentot, brought forth by a filthy mother who would nurse me in her 'kraal', and teach me to bow down to Pagan gods, quite as easily as to have given me a pious mother, who would each morning and night bend her knee in prayer on my behalf? Or, might he not, if he had pleased, have given me some profligate to have been my parent, from whose lips I might have early heard fearful, filthy, and obscene language? Might he not have placed me where I should have had a drunken father, who would have immured me in a very dungeon of ignorance, and brought me up in the chains of crime? Was it not God's Providence that I had so happy a lot, that both my parents were his children, and endeavoured to train me up in the fear of the Lord?

LOVED BY GOD BEFORE WE WERE BORN

John Newton used to tell a whimsical story, and laugh at it, too, of a good woman who said, in order to prove the doctrine of election, 'Ah! sir, the Lord must have loved me before I was born, or else he would not have seen anything in me to love afterwards.' I am sure it is true in my case; I believe the doctrine of election, because I am quite certain that, if God had not chosen me, I should never have chosen him; and I am sure he chose me before I was born, or else he never would have chosen me afterwards; and he must have elected me for reasons unknown to me, for I never could find any reason in myself why he should have looked upon me with special love.

So I am forced to accept that great biblical doctrine. I recollect an Arminian brother telling me that he had read the Scriptures through a score or more times, and could never find the doctrine of election in them. He added that he was sure he would have done so if it had been there, for he read the Word on his knees. I said to him, 'I think you read the Bible in a very uncomfortable posture, and if you had read it in your easy chair, you would have been more likely to understand it. Pray, by all means, and the more, the better, but it is a piece of superstition to think there is anything in the posture in which a man puts himself for reading: and as to reading through the Bible twenty times without having found anything about the doctrine of election, the wonder is that you found anything at all: you must have galloped through it at such a rate that you were not likely to have any intelligible idea of the meaning of the Scriptures.'

If it would be marvellous to see one river leap up from the earth full-grown, what would it be to gaze upon a vast spring from which all the rivers of the earth should at once come bubbling up, a million of them born at a birth? What a vision would it be! Who can conceive it? And yet the love of God is that fountain, from which all the rivers of mercy, which have ever gladdened our race – all the rivers of grace in time, and of glory hereafter – take their rise. My soul, stand thou at that sacred fountain-head, and adore and magnify, for ever and ever, God, even our Father, who hath loved us! In the very beginning, when this great universe lay in the mind of God, like unborn forests in the acorn cup; long ere the echoes awoke the solitudes; before the mountains were brought forth; and long ere the light flashed through the sky, God loved his chosen creatures. Before there was any created being – when the ether was not fanned by an angel's wing, when space itself had not an existence, when there was nothing save God alone – even then, in that loneliness of Deity, and in that deep quiet and profundity, his bowels moved with love for his chosen. Their names were written on his heart, and then were they dear to his soul. Jesus loved his people before the foundation of the world – even from eternity! And when he called me by his grace, he said to me, 'I have loved *thee* with an everlasting love: therefore with loving-kindness have I drawn thee.'

PURCHASED BY JESUS' BLOOD

Then, in the fullness of time, he purchased me with his blood; he let his heart run out in one deep gaping wound for me long ere I loved him. Yea, when he first came to me, did I not spurn him? When he knocked at the door, and asked for entrance, did I not drive him away, and do despite to his grace? Ah, I can remember that I full often did so until, at last, by the power of his effectual grace, he said, 'I must, I will come in'; and then he turned my heart, and made me love him. But even till now I should have resisted him, had it not been for his grace. Well, then, since he purchased me when I was dead in sins, does it not follow, as a consequence necessary and logical, that he must have loved me first? Did my Saviour die for me because I believed on him? No; I was not then in existence; I had then no being. Could the Saviour, therefore, have died because I had faith, when I myself was not yet born? Could that have been possible? Could that have been the origin of the Saviour's love towards me? Oh! no; my Saviour died for me long before I believed. 'But', says someone, 'he foresaw that you would have faith; and, therefore, he loved you.'

What did he foresee about my faith? Did he foresee that I should get that faith myself, and that I should believe on him of myself? No; Christ could not foresee that, because no Christian man will ever say that faith came of itself without the gift and without the working of the Holy Spirit. I have met with a great many believers, and talked with them about this matter; but I never knew one who could put his hand on his heart, and say, 'I believed in Jesus without the assistance of the Holy Spirit.'

THE HEART IS THE PROBLEM

I am bound to the doctrine of the depravity of the human heart, because I find myself depraved in heart, and have daily proofs that in my flesh there dwelleth no good thing. If God enters into covenant with unfallen man, man is so insignificant a creature that it must be an act of gracious condescension on the Lord's part; but if God enters into covenant with *sinful* man, he is then so offensive a creature that it must be, on God's part, an act of pure, free, rich, sovereign grace. When the Lord entered into covenant with me, I am sure that it was all of grace, nothing else but grace. When I remember what a den of unclean beasts and birds my heart was, and how strong was my unrenewed will, how obstinate and rebellious against the sovereignty of the Divine rule, I always feel inclined to take the very lowest room in my Father's house, and when I enter heaven, it will be to go among the less than the least of all saints, and with the chief of sinners.

'SALVATION IS OF THE LORD'

The late lamented Mr Denham has put, at the foot of his portrait, a most admirable text, *'Salvation is of the Lord.'* That is just an epitome of Calvinism; it is the sum and substance of it. If anyone should ask me what I mean by a Calvinist, I should reply, 'He is one who says, Salvation is of the Lord.' I cannot find in Scripture any other doctrine than this. It is the essence of the Bible. 'He *only* is my rock and my salvation.' Tell me anything contrary to this truth, and it will be a heresy; tell me a heresy, and I shall find its essence here, that it has departed from this great, this fundamental, this rock-truth, 'God is my rock and my salvation.' What is the heresy of Rome, but the addition of something to the perfect merits of Jesus Christ – the bringing in of the works of the flesh, to assist in our justification? And what is the heresy of Arminianism but the addition of something to the work of the Redeemer? Every heresy, if brought to the touchstone, will discover itself here. I have my own private opinion that there is no such thing as preaching Christ and him crucified, unless we preach what nowadays is called Calvinism. It is a nickname to call it Calvinism; Calvinism is the gospel, and nothing else. I do not believe we can preach the gospel, if we do not preach justification by faith, without works; nor unless we preach the sovereignty of God in his dispensation of grace; nor unless we exalt the electing, unchangeable, eternal, immutable, conquering love of Jehovah; nor do I think we can preach the gospel, unless we base it upon the special and particular redemption of his elect and chosen people which Christ wrought out upon the cross; nor can I comprehend a gospel which lets saints fall away after they are called, and suffers the children of God to be burned in the fires of damnation after having once believed in Jesus. Such a gospel I abhor.

> If ever it should come to pass,
>   That sheep of Christ might fall away,
> My fickle, feeble soul, alas!
>   Would fall a thousand times a day.

WHY SAINTS PERSEVERE

If one dear saint of God had perished, so might all; if one of the covenant ones be lost, so may all be; and then there is no gospel promise true, but the Bible is a lie, and there is nothing in it worth my acceptance. I will be an infidel at once when I can believe that a saint of God can ever fall finally. If God hath loved me once, then he will love me forever. God has a mastermind; he arranged everything in his gigantic intellect long before he did it; and once having settled it, he never alters it, 'This shall be done', saith he, and the iron hand of destiny marks it down, and it is brought to pass. 'This is my purpose', and it stands, nor can earth or hell alter it. 'This is my decree', saith he, 'promulgate it, ye holy angels; rend it down from the gate of heaven, ye devils, if ye can; but ye cannot alter the decree, it shall stand forever.' God altereth not his plans; why should he? He is almighty, and therefore can perform his pleasure. Why should he? He is the All-wise, and therefore cannot have planned wrongly. Why should he? He is the everlasting God, and therefore cannot die before his plan is accomplished. Why should he change? Ye worthless atoms of earth, ephemera of a day, ye creeping insects upon this bay-leaf of existence, ye may change your plans, but he shall never, never change *his*. Has he told me that his plan is to save me? If so, I am forever safe.

> My name from the palms of His hands
>   Eternity will not erase;
> Impressed on His heart it remains,
>   In marks of indelible grace.

HOW TO BE A HAPPY CHRISTIAN

I do not know how some people, who believe that a Christian can fall from grace, manage to be happy. It must be a very commendable thing in them to be able to get through a day without despair. If I did not believe the doctrine of the final perseverance of the saints, I think I should be of all men the most miserable, because I should lack any ground of comfort. I could not say, whatever state of heart I came into, that I should be like a well-spring of water, whose stream fails not; I should rather have to take the comparison of an intermittent spring, that might stop on a sudden, or a reservoir, which I had no reason to expect would always be full. I believe that the happiest of Christians and the truest of Christians are those who never dare to doubt God, but who take his Word simply as it stands, and believe it, and ask no questions, just feeling assured that if God has said it, it will be so.

I bear my willing testimony that I have no reason, nor even the shadow of a reason, to doubt my Lord, and I challenge heaven, and earth, and hell, to bring any proof that God is untrue. From the depths of hell I call the fiends, and from this earth I call the tried and afflicted believers, and to heaven I appeal, and challenge the long experience of the blood-washed host, and there is not to be found in the three realms a single person who can bear witness to one fact which can disprove the faithfulness of God, or weaken his claim to be trusted by his servants. There are many things that may or may not happen, but this I know *shall* happen –

> He shall present my soul,
>   Unblemished and complete,
> Before the glory of His face,
>   With joys divinely great.

All the purposes of man have been defeated, but not the purposes of God. The promises of man may be broken – many of them are made to be broken – but the promises of God shall all be fulfilled. He is a promise-maker, but he never was a promise-breaker; he is a promise-keeping God, and every one of his people shall prove it to be so. This is my grateful, personal confidence, 'The Lord *will* perfect that which concerneth *me*' – unworthy *me*, lost and ruined *me*. He will yet save *me*; and –

> I, among the blood-washed throng,
> Shall wave the palm, and wear the crown,
>   And shout loud victory.

I go to a land which the plough of earth hath never up-turned, where it is greener than earth's best pastures, and richer than her most abundant harvests ever saw. I go to a building of more gorgeous architecture than man hath ever builded; it is not of mortal design; it is 'a building of God, a house not made with hands, eternal in the heavens'. All I shall know and enjoy in heaven, will be given to me by the Lord, and I shall say, when at last I appear before him –

> Grace all the work shall crown
>   Through everlasting days;
>   It lays in heaven the topmost stone,
>   And well deserves the praise.

'THE PRECIOUS BLOOD OF CHRIST'

I know there are some who think it necessary to their system of theology to limit the merit of the blood of Jesus: if my theological system needed such a limitation, I would cast it to the winds. I cannot, I dare not allow the thought to find a lodging in my mind, it seems so near akin to blasphemy. In Christ's finished work I see an ocean of merit; my plummet finds no bottom, my eye discovers no shore. There must be sufficient efficacy in the blood of Christ, if God had so willed it, to have saved not only all in this world, but all in ten thousand worlds, had they transgressed their Maker's law. Once admit infinity into the matter, and limit is out of the question. Having a Divine Person for an offering, it is not consistent to conceive of limited value; bound and measure are terms inapplicable to the Divine sacrifice.

The intent of the Divine purpose fixes the *application* of the infinite offering, but does not change it into a finite work. Think of the numbers upon whom God has bestowed his grace already. Think of the countless hosts in heaven: if thou wert introduced there today, thou wouldst find it as easy to tell the stars, or the sands of the sea, as to count the multitudes that are before the throne even now. They have come from the East, and from the West, from the North, and from the South, and they are sitting down with Abraham, and with Isaac, and with Jacob in the kingdom of God; and beside those in heaven, think of the saved ones on earth. Blessed be God, his elect on earth are to be counted by millions, I believe, and the days are coming, brighter days than these, when there shall be multitudes upon multitudes brought to know the Saviour, and to rejoice in him. The Father's love is not for a few only, but for an exceeding great company. 'A great multitude, which no man could number', will be found in heaven. A man can reckon up to very high figures; set to work your Newtons, your mightiest calculators, and they can count great numbers, but God and God alone can tell the multitude of his redeemed. I believe there will be more in heaven than in hell. If anyone asks me why I think so, I answer, because Christ, in everything, is to 'have the pre-eminence', and I cannot conceive how he could have the pre-eminence if there are to be more in the dominions of Satan than in paradise.

Moreover, I have never read that there is to be in hell a great multitude, which no man could number. I rejoice to know that the souls of all infants, as soon as they die, speed their way to paradise. Think what a multitude there is of them! Then there are already in heaven un-numbered myriads of the spirits of just men made perfect – the redeemed of all nations, and kindreds, and people, and tongues up till now; and there are better times coming, when the religion of Christ shall be universal; when –

> He shall reign from pole to pole,
> With illimitable sway;

when whole kingdoms shall bow down before him, and nations shall be born in a day, and in the thousand years of the great millennial state there will be enough saved to make up all the deficiencies of the thousands of years that have gone before.

Christ shall be Master everywhere, and his praise shall be sounded in every land. Christ shall have the pre-eminence at last; his train shall be far larger than that which shall attend the chariot of the grim monarch of hell.

A UNIVERSAL ATONEMENT?

Some persons love the doctrine of universal atonement because they say, 'It is so beautiful. It is a lovely idea that Christ should have died for all men; it commends itself', they say, 'to the instincts of humanity; there is something in it full of joy and beauty.' I admit there is, but beauty may be often associated with falsehood. There is much which I might admire in the theory of universal redemption, but I will just show what the supposition necessarily involves. If Christ on his cross intended to save every man, then he intended to save those who were lost before he died. If the doctrine be true, that he died for all men, then he died for some who were in hell before he came into this world, for doubtless there were even then myriads there who had been cast away because of their sins. Once again, if it was Christ's intention to save all men, how deplorably has he been disappointed, for we have his own testimony that there is a lake which burneth with fire and brimstone, and into that pit of woe have been cast some of the very persons who, according to the theory of universal redemption, were bought with his blood. That seems to me a conception a thousand times more repulsive than any of those consequences which are said to be associated with the Calvinistic and Christian doctrine of special and particular redemption. To think that my Saviour died for men who were or are in hell, seems a supposition too horrible for me to entertain.

To imagine for a moment that he was the Substitute for all the sons of men, and that God, having first punished the Substitute, afterwards punished the sinners themselves, seems to conflict with all my ideas of Divine justice. That Christ should offer an atonement and satisfaction for the sins of all men, and that afterwards some of those very men should be punished for the sins for which Christ had already atoned, appears to me to be the most monstrous iniquity that could ever have been imputed to Saturn, to Janus, to the goddess of the Thugs, or to the most diabolical heathen deities. God forbid that we should ever think thus of Jehovah, the just and wise and good!

WHAT'S IN A NAME?

There is no soul living who holds more firmly to the doctrines of grace than I do, and if any man asks me whether

I am ashamed to be called a Calvinist, I answer – 'I wish to be called nothing but a Christian'; but if you ask me, do I hold the doctrinal views which were held by John Calvin, I reply, 'I do in the main hold them, and rejoice to avow it.'

But far be it from me even to imagine that Zion contains none but Calvinistic Christians within her walls, or that there are none saved who do not hold our views. Most atrocious things have been spoken about the character and spiritual condition of John Wesley, the modern prince of Arminians. I can only say concerning him that, while I detest many of the doctrines which he preached, yet for the man himself I have a reverence second to no Wesleyan; and if there were wanted two apostles to be added to the number of the twelve, I do not believe that there could be found two men more fit to be so added than George Whitefield and John Wesley. The character of John Wesley stands beyond all imputation for self-sacrifice, zeal, holiness, and communion with God; he lived far above the ordinary level of common Christians, and was one 'of whom the world was not worthy'. I believe there are multitudes of men who cannot see these truths, or, at least, cannot see them in the way in which we put them, who nevertheless have received Christ as their Saviour, and are as dear to the heart of the God of grace as the soundest Calvinist in or out of heaven.

CALVINISM AND HYPER-CALVINISM – WHAT'S THE DIFFERENCE?

I do not think I differ from any of my Hyper-Calvinistic brethren in what I do believe, but I differ from them in what they do not believe. I do not hold any less than they do, but I hold a little more, and, I think, a little more of the truth revealed in the Scriptures. Not only are there a few cardinal doctrines, by which we can steer our ship North, South, East, or West, but as we study the Word, we shall begin to learn something about the North-west and North-east, and all else that lies between the four cardinal points.

The system of truth revealed in the Scriptures is not simply one straight line, but two; and no man will ever get a right view of the gospel until he knows how to look at the two lines at once. For instance, I read in one Book of the Bible, 'The Spirit and the bride say, Come. And let him that heareth say, Come. And let him that is athirst come. And whosoever will, let him take the water of life freely.' Yet I am taught, in another part of the same inspired Word, that, 'it is not of him that willeth, nor of him that runneth, but of God that sheweth mercy.' I see, in one place, God in providence presiding over all, and yet I see, and I cannot help seeing, that man acts as he pleases, and that God has left his actions, in a great measure, to his own free-will. Now, if I were to declare that man was so free to act that there was no control of God over his actions, I should be driven very near to atheism; and if, on the other hand, I should declare that God so over-rules all things that man is not free enough to be responsible, I should be driven at once into Antinomianism or fatalism.

That God predestines, and yet that man is responsible, are two facts that few can see clearly. They are believed to be inconsistent and contradictory to each other. If, then, I find taught in one part of the Bible that everything is foreordained, *that is true;* and if I find, in another Scripture, that man is responsible for all his actions, *that is true;* and it is only my folly that leads me to imagine that these two truths can ever contradict each other. I do not believe they can ever be welded into one upon any earthly anvil, but they certainly shall be one in eternity. They are two lines that are so nearly parallel, that the human mind which pursues them farthest will never discover that they converge, but they do converge, and they will meet somewhere in eternity, close to the throne of God, whence all truth doth spring.

'SHALL WE SIN THAT GRACE MAY ABOUND? GOD FORBID!'

It is often said that the doctrines we believe have a tendency to lead us to sin. I have heard it asserted most positively, that those high doctrines which we love, and which we find in the Scriptures, are licentious ones. I do not know who will have the hardihood to make that assertion, when they consider that the holiest of men have been believers in them. I ask the man who dares to say that Calvinism is a licentious religion, what he thinks of the character of Augustine, or Calvin, or Whitefield, who in successive ages were the great exponents of the system of grace; or what will he say of the Puritans, whose works are full of them? Had a man been an Arminian in those days, he would have been accounted the vilest heretic breathing, but now *we* are looked upon as the heretics, and they as the orthodox. *We* have gone back to the old school; *we* can trace our descent from the apostles. It is that vein of free-grace, running through the sermonizing of Baptists, which has saved us as a denomination.

Were it not for that, we should not stand where we are today. We can run a golden line up to Jesus Christ himself, through a holy succession of mighty fathers, who all held these glorious truths; and we can ask concerning them, 'Where will you find holier and better men in the world?' No doctrine is so calculated to preserve a man from sin as the doctrine of the grace of God. Those who have called it 'a licentious doctrine' did not know anything at all about it. Poor ignorant things, they little knew that their own vile stuff was the most licentious doctrine under heaven. If they knew the grace of God in truth, they would soon see that there was no preservative from lying like a knowledge that we are elect of God from the foundation of the world.

There is nothing like a belief in my eternal perseverance, and the immutability of my Father's affection, which can keep me near to him from a motive of simple gratitude. Nothing makes a man so virtuous as belief of the truth. A lying doctrine will soon beget a lying practice. A man cannot have an erroneous belief without by-and-by having an erroneous life. I believe the one thing naturally begets the other.

Of all men, those have the most disinterested piety, the sublimest reverence, the most ardent devotion, who believe that they are saved by grace, without works, through faith, and that not of themselves, it is the gift of God. Christians should take heed, and see that it always is so, lest by any means Christ should be crucified afresh, and put to an open shame.

OTHER SPURGEON TITLES FROM THE BANNER OF TRUTH TRUST

C. H. Spurgeon's Autobiography
> Volume 1: *The Early Years, 1834–1860*
>> ISBN 0 85151 076 0 580 pp. cloth-bound
> Volume 2, *The Full Harvest, 1861–1892*
>> ISBN 0 85151 182 1 536 pp. cloth-bound

Advice for Seekers
> ISBN 0 85151 651 3 96 pp. paperback

An All-Round Ministry
> ISBN 0 85151 181 3 416 pp. paperback

Lectures to My Students
> ISBN 978 0 85151 966 1 928 pp. cloth-bound

Letters of C. H. Spurgeon, Edited by Iain H. Murray
> ISBN 0 85151 606 8 192 pp. paperback

Majesty in Misery:

   Volume 1: *Dark Gethsemane*

   ISBN 0 85151 904 0 288 pp. cloth-bound

   Volume 2: *The Judgment Hall*

   ISBN 0 85151 915 6 320 pp. cloth-bound

   Volume 3: *Calvary's Mournful Mountain*

   ISBN 0 85151 916 4 400 pp. cloth-bound

The Pastor in Prayer

   ISBN 0 85151 850 8 192 pp. cloth-bound

Revival Year Sermons

   ISBN 0 85151 703 X 96 pp. paperback

The Forgotten Spurgeon, Iain H. Murray

   ISBN 0 85151 156 2 256 pp. paperback

Spurgeon v. Hyper-Calvinism, Iain H. Murray

   ISBN 0 85151 692 0 184 pp. paperback

Spurgeon: A New Biography, Arnold Dallimore

   ISBN 0 85151 451 0 272 pp. large paperback

Other booklets in this series from The Banner of Truth Trust:

For details of other helpful publications and
free illustrated catalogue please write to

THE BANNER OF TRUTH TRUST

3 Murrayfield Road,
Edinburgh EH12 6EL
UK

P O Box 621, Carlisle,
Pennsylvania 17013,
USA

www.banneroftruth.co.uk

Sleeping Lord Beattie

The Contrary Fairy Tales: Book 1

Em Taylor

i

Copyright

Cover Art: Verónica Muñoz Fernández and Em Taylor

Editor: Maria Lazarou at Obsessed by Books Designs

Dedication

To Suzie

Thank you for everything you do for me. For all your hard work, your encouragement, your "nagging" and your support. I couldn't have got through this past year without your help and the Contrary Fairy Tales would never have come into being without you.

You can be a pain in my arse anytime you want—but not in that way. Reserve that for Lord Byron.

Love you loads,

Em xx

Author's Note

In 1815, Mount Tambora, which is located on a remote island in the Indian Ocean, erupted, causing a huge ash cloud to shroud much of the upper atmosphere. This gradually started to affect the weather. A particularly cold winter between 1815 and 1816 led to a dreadfully cold, wet spring and summer, resulting in a bad harvest over most of the Northern hemisphere.

There was much famine and civil discontent. It was during that summer that Lord Byron, exiled from Switzerland, hosted a number of friends. Unable to take part in much outdoor activity, Byron and his friends had writing competitions to write scary stories. With that Mary Shelley's Frankenstein was created. Or so the story goes.

There is not a lot of information to be found with regards to England and the difficulties faced during that year. This, however, is a work of fiction.

Prologue

Gideon Beattie, or Viscount Beattie as he was known, trudged through the mud, carrying three large planks of wood. They were needed to mend one of his stables. The place was falling apart. Everything was falling apart. Gideon hadn't realised just how bad things had got in the past few years. His father had allowed the estate to fall into rack and ruin. Many staff had left due to the fact his father hadn't paid them. Gideon couldn't blame them. If only his father had told him. He could have helped.

Gideon had made a modest fortune in the years during and after university. With the money his father had given him monthly, he'd lived the life of a young buck but had also saved and invested wisely. He had a bit of a talent for sniffing out a good investment and some of his investments, especially in the shipping trade, had paid off handsomely. He also knew when to quit when he ventured into a gaming hell. If you are losing quit. If you win big, quit.

It seemed this had not been something he'd inherited from his father's side of the family. The man had drunk, gambled away the family fortune and after one final bad investment, Gideon's father took his own life. Gideon's sister had found him, face down, on his desk, a bottle of laudanum spilt over the surface. He'd taken enough of the opiate to kill a horse; the doctor had said.

No one in the house had said anything and against church rules, Gideon's father had been laid to rest in the family graveyard, next to the church on the estate. The fact they had lied to the vicar still pricked at Gideon's conscience, but better that than upset Sophia any further.

He walked into the stable and dropped the planks of wood. He'd much rather have done this with the animals out in the fields but the weather this year had been awful. Cold, wet and damp. Everyone was reporting failed crops and the newspapers said that people in Wales were rioting as a result of food shortages. Some people were predicting the beginning of the prophecies from the Revelation of Saint John the Divine in the Holy Bible. He believed it was just a year of bad weather and suspected it had nothing to do with God or apocalyptic prophecies.

Fixing the stable was going to upset the animals if he was hammering away at the wood in their vicinity, but there was nothing else for it. The weather was too awful to put them outside and he couldn't leave the stables in such disrepair any longer.

He picked up the hammer, a large nail and placed the wood over the large gap in the horse's stall. Honestly, it was a miracle the beast hadn't escaped yet.

As he started to hammer, Caesar, his black gelding started to neigh.

"Hush, Caesar. Tis fine," Gideon crooned, hoping the animal would recognise his voice and be calmed. He took a second nail. Best to hammer each one in a little and get the plank on straight at first. He might not be used to doing manual labour, but as a boy, he'd watched the men around the estate and sometimes asked to help them. They had occasionally obliged when no one was looking. Gideon suspected it was more to get peace than because they liked the young baron.

As he hammered in the second nail, Caesar stamped his foot and snorted.

"Easy boy. It's me. I'm just sorting your stall to stop the wind coming in. Don't you want that? Must be cold in here at night."

Everything that happened next seemed to happen so quickly that Gideon could not have prevented it, had he tried. Caesar whinnied and reared up, his hooves catching the back of Gideon's head as he came back down. Gideon fell against the upright stake of the stall, his hand catching on a nail. He pulled it free and was aware of the upright post giving way and a creaking sound. Dirt and dust fell around him then pain like he had never experienced cracked his head. As the light faded he heard himself as if from a distance.

"'S fine, Caesar. Shh boy!"

Chapter 1

"I do not need to be chaperoned, Aunt. I shall be with Sophia and her brother is asleep. He is most likely dying. He won't wake up. He has been like this for three weeks. She shall be my chaperone. She is a widow so she is quite respectable."

Lady Emily Beresford, the sister of the Earl of Whitsnow was determined. She would not be remaining in her aunt's townhouse in London one moment longer than was necessary. Her friend needed her. Her brother had insisted that once again she go to town in search of a husband, but honestly, it was pointless. No man wanted her. She knew what they said about her. The whispers behind her back. Oh, she was pretty enough, she supposed, and she had a good dowry. She'd had a few men showing interest in her first few seasons because of her large dowry but not now. Lady Clumsy—that's the moniker they had given her because she trod on gentlemen's toes when she danced. She also invariably spilt her drink on her gown. She almost never accepted drinks at balls now. How debasing having such a nickname.

Now she was three and twenty years old and she was almost officially on the shelf.

"You shall never find a husband at this rate, Emily."

"I doubt I shall find a husband anyway, Aunt. No one is vying for my hand in marriage. No one is interested."

"What about Cedric Onslow."

"The illegitimate son of the Duke of Hartsmere?"

"You can't afford to be fussy at your age, Emily."

"I can afford to be fussier than Mr Onslow. He's a dandy. He wears inexpressibles. You can see *everything.*"

"How would you know. You should not be looking at men below the waist."

"It is hard not to, Aunt. It's difficult to ignore."

"Hmm, well, perhaps even I would draw the line at Mr Onslow, on reflection. Perhaps we should contact the Duke of Hartsmere and see if his legitimate son, the Earl of Cindermaine, wants a wife."

"He is never seen in town because of his ill health. I doubt he would be interested."

"No harm in asking."

"Perhaps not." Emily shook her head. "However, I am going to Herefordshire to see Lady

Rutherford, and you cannot stop me. I shall take my maid and obviously, there will be a coachman and a stable boy. We shall be fine."

"I forbid it, Emily."

"I am three and twenty, Aunt. You cannot forbid it. Besides, I already wrote to tell her I shall visit. If you do not let me go, I shall take the mail coach."

Of course, Emily would never consider taking the mail coach and Aunt Gertrude would never countenance such a thing but Aunt Gertrude believed Emily to be 'a bit of a hoyden', so Emily knew her Aunt would half expect her to do it.

"I shall summon Robert."

"Robert is in Cumberland, Aunt. You know he cannot get here in time to stop me. I leave early tomorrow morning. I do hope you will wish me well."

"I shall do no such thing. Have you seen the rain? You shall drown in the mud no doubt."

Emily blanched. It was a concern. She had heard so much of the terrible weather conditions and the poor state of the roads. She may very well end up in trouble, but Sophia seemed so lost in the pages of her letter and Emily knew she had to get to her friend and comfort her.

She left the room but as she went she turned to her aunt. "I must go. I would want someone with me if Robert was dying."

∞ ∞ ∞

Emily walked down to breakfast the next morning, determined not to argue with her aunt. There was no point. She would simply smile and wish her a cheerful goodbye and thank her for her concern. There was nothing else for it.

When she walked into the breakfast room, Aunt Gertrude was sitting eating toast and raspberry jam. What caught Emily's attention, however, was what Aunt Gertrude was wearing. She wore her green carriage dress.

"Good morning, Aunt."

"There is not much good about this morning, Emily. It is still raining."

Emily glanced through the French doors and grimaced. "It has been raining every day since March I think."

"We had a few nice days in May I believe."

"Oh yes. I do recall. You appear to have put on your carriage dress this morning, Aunt."

"That is what one usually wears when one is going on a long carriage ride, is it not, Emily?"

"It is. Are you going somewhere nice?"

"I have no idea. Is the Beattie estate nice?"

"You are coming with me?" Emily nearly dropped the teapot she had just picked up.

"Don't be ridiculous dear. I cannot have you wandering about the countryside on your own. Robert would never forgive me."

"But you'll miss the entertainments of the Season."

Aunt Gertrude rolled her eyes.

"Emily, my dear, the Season is completely washed out this year. No one is feeling frivolous and happy. No one cares about the gossip and the jolly japes. No one is getting up to any jolly japes for that matter. Everyone just wants to sit at home by the fireside and read or write letters. It really is rather miserable. I would rather be with you, and, as you said yesterday, you would wish someone would be there for you if Robert was ill and perhaps dying."

Emily nodded. "Yes, I would. I appreciate the offer but please do not feel you ought. I can go on my own."

"It would be a pleasure. You are a true friend to this young lady. What is her name?"

"Sophia. She is Lady Rutherford. Her brother is Viscount Beattie. She is the widow of the late Lord Rutherford who died just five months ago."

"Ah, I see. Perhaps he is not at death's door. We shall see when we get there."

Emily hurried to the sideboard to fill a plate of food for breakfast. Aunt Gertrude was not a bad old stick really. In fact, she had a heart of gold. She was just a little strict and had rather old-fashioned views about how young ladies should behave. But Emily felt a warm glow and, she had to admit to herself, a little less apprehensive about this trip now that she would have company. She had been a little scared to venture out on her own, albeit with a maid and a coachman to look after her.

With Aunt Gertrude snoring away beside her all the way to Herefordshire, Emily knew she wouldn't feel lonely until she met her friend again.

Chapter 2

It took four days to get to Herefordshire. It was a long journey anyway, but the weather conditions just made it longer. Emily insisted that Martha, her maid, ride inside the coach with them. She couldn't do anything for the stable hand and her coachman but they both assured her that they were fine and a little rain wouldn't kill them.

It was more than a little rain. It was torrential.

As expected, Aunt Gertrude slept through the journey. Emily had been wise enough to put a couple of books under the seat of the carriage to keep her occupied and Martha had brought along her crochet.

"What are you making?" She asked Martha.

"Lacy doilies for under the vases on my ma's sideboard." Emily peered at the little circle in Martha's hand. She had barely started but already Emily could see the intricate pattern forming.

"Oh my. I did not realise crocheting was so..."

"Delicate? Pretty?"

"I think of it as being warm shawls for winter."

"Oh, you can make lace shawls for the summer. We just make the warm stuff because we have no need for the fancy stuff, my lady."

"But you could make the fancy ones and sell them to the ladies of the *ton.* They would pay handsomely for work such as this."

"Like this?" She pulled a doily out of her bag that she had already made. It was intricate and finely made.

"It's beautiful, Martha." Emily allowed the thin lacy material to run through her gloved fingers. "Would you teach me how to crochet?"

Martha pulled her head back in shock. "Oh, my lady, I don't think that would be right."

"Oh, I suppose it would not."

"What would not be right?" asked Aunt Gertrude, clearly having just woken up.

"Oh, I... Martha makes these beautiful items by crocheting. I foolishly asked her to teach me."

Aunt Gertrude took the doily from Emily and considered it. "It is a beautiful piece. It is a long way to Herefordshire, my dear. You may as well put your time to good use. Perhaps Martha would be willing to teach you as we travel." She looked over her spectacles at Martha.

The maid nodded furiously. "Of course, my lady. It would be my pleasure."

"That is settled then. I shall go back to watching the scenery."

Emily smiled at her aunt. Watching the scenery indeed. The woman had been no more watching the scenery than she had been playing cricket on the village green.

∞ ∞ ∞

Emily was bored. It was now nearing the end of the third day of their carriage ride. She didn't understand how Aunt Gertrude could sleep so much. Crochet was much harder than she thought and she began to wonder if Martha was a witch. Not that she believed in witches of course, but crochet seemed like it must be a dark art. The whole concept eluded her. Martha's wrist worked furiously as she created yet another doily.

Just then shouts from outside drew her attention as the carriage came to a halt. They hadn't pulled in to a coaching inn. She could tell they were still on the road. Her coachman was shouting angrily. What on earth could be going on? She was about to nudge Aunt Gertrude awake when the door flew open and a man with his face covered in a handkerchief waved a pistol at them.

"Give me yer jewels and money." Emily's heart started to race and her mouth went dry. She had no idea what to do or say. She had on her pearls but how did one deal with highwaymen. Should she fight, refuse, do as she was told?

The man's dirty blond hair stuck out from under his tricorn hat. It was overly long. His voice had a slight tremble to it as he waved the pistol about wildly. He was soaked to the skin. Had it not been for the fact he was in the process of stealing from them, Emily would have felt sorry for him. He must be freezing.

"Huh!" Aunt Gertrude jumped awake. "What's going on?" she asked in her imperious way.

The man rolled his eyes. "I'm a highwayman. Give me yer jewels and money."

"Oh of course. Emily. All the jewels and money are in the blue reticule under your seat. Give it to the man."

Emily gasped but something in Aunt Gertrude's voice made her obey, and the fact the man was pointing a pistol at her meant Emily did not wish to argue the point. Now was not the time for debate. She didn't, however, offer to hand over the pearls that were around her neck and could not be seen under her pelisse. She handed him the bag and the highwayman looked inside. She would wait to see if he asked if they had any jewels on before offering. She noted that Aunt Gertrude did not offer up the jewels she was wearing either.

"This is a nice stash. Thank you kindly my ladies."

"You are a brute. You should be ashamed of yourself. I hope your mother is ashamed of you." Aunt Gertrude's face was red with indignation.

"She likely is, Your Ladyship. She likely is." With that, he closed the door and disappeared into the trees next to the road.

"He will burn in hell," muttered Aunt Gertrude.

"Oh Aunt, all your jewels." Aunt Gertrude tapped on the roof of the carriage to tell the driver to go on. Then she turned a gleeful grin on Emily.

"Don't be ridiculous, Emily, my dear. Do you honestly think I would have handed over my jewels to that little weasel? He has a few coins and some jewels made of paste. I really am surprised these highwaymen haven't worked out this trick yet. Though he did not seem the cleverest of fellows, did he? He did not even ask for the jewels we were wearing.

"I did notice that. I was waiting for him to ask if I had any on my person."

"He is an imbecile, obviously." She sniffed disdainfully as if she had expected more. A higher class of highwayman maybe.

Aunt Gertrude nestled back into her seat and continued to "watch the scenery" as if nothing had happened. What a strange little occurrence. It was almost as if nothing had happened. They had been robbed but Aunt Gertrude had handed over fake jewels and gone right back to sleep.

Just wait until she told Sophia. She caught Martha's gaze. That was more like it. The maid's eyes were popping out of her head.

"Now we know how to deal with highwaymen, Martha."

"We do indeed. Perhaps the Prince Regent should have sent Her Ladyship over to fight Mr

Napoleon instead of sending The Duke of Wellington." Emily stifled a laugh.

"Don't say that in front of any gentlemen. They would be rather offended to hear someone suggest a mere woman to be braver than the Duke."

"I'm sure the Duke was very brave and clever. I just think your aunt is too."

"Yes, she is. And I am very pleased she came along as I would not have known what to do"

"We would have managed."

"Perhaps but not with such aplomb and we would have had to give them real jewels and more money."

"That would have been a shame."

"It would have. We do still have one more night to pay the inn and what if one of the horses go lame. I do have sympathy if that man needs to feed his family, Martha, but we do need to get to our destination so that we can help my friend."

"I know, my lady. I was not suggesting otherwise."

Martha looked back down at her crochet and Emily turned back to her book. She understood that times were hard. This year in particular. She read the newspaper and not just the gossip columns. She knew the weather was impacting the crops and yields. She wasn't heartless. Why else would she be making this perilous journey to comfort her friend?

Tears burned at the back of her eyes but she closed her lids and willed them away. Martha just had a different perspective. She hadn't meant to sound harsh. Things would all seem better once they got to Little Foxton in Herefordshire.

Chapter 3

As had been the way of it all year, it was raining when they arrived at Beattie Park near Little Foxton. The grass was water-logged and the flowers had never quite managed to bloom. The gardens were in quite a sorry state, but that seemed to be the way for most of England. Though it did seem worse out here than it had nearer London.

Sophia had welcomed them with open arms. Though she had been a little taken aback by the arrival of Aunt Gertrude, she had been pleased that Emily had been accompanied on the journey—especially once Emily recounted their run-in with the highwayman.

"Oh, come now, Emily, he was just a boy. I doubt he knew how to shoot that pistol."

"He seemed rather scary to me, Aunt."

"That's because you are just a girl yourself, dear. Once you have a few more years of experience you'll see bravado for what it is."

Emily doubted that she would ever be as calm and collected as Aunt Gertrude had been when having a pistol waved in her face.

Sophia had organised tea and cakes and they were all sitting in the drawing room, the fire blazing, warming them up after the long, arduous journey.

"Thank you so much for coming, and Lady Wardlaw, I do appreciate you accompanying Emily. I was quite beside myself when I received her letter to tell me she was visiting."

"It was not well done of her to frighten you like that Lady Rutherford, especially not in your condition." Aunt Gertrude looked at Sophia and it was then that Emily realised that Sophia's belly was distended. Her gown covered it but there was definitely a baby bump there.

"You are increasing? But you had not told me."

"I planned to tell you in my last letter but with everything that happened with Gideon, it completely slipped my mind."

"How can a large belly completely slip your mind?"

"Emily! Please have some manners." Aunt Gertrude was almost purple with embarrassment. Emily's cheeks heated with shame.

"I apologise."

Sophia laughed. "There is no need. We are friends and no one else is here. It is difficult to forget. I do wish it wasn't so, but at least Viscount Rutherford has his heir even if he did not live long enough for me to tell him. His nephew is not best pleased with me."

"How did he die, dear. I heard it was sudden."

"He was rather old. They said it was his heart. Though I don't think the cold winter helped. He had been suffering from a terrible cough for months."

"I don't know how you could have married such an elderly man, Sophia. I really do not," said Emily, without considering her words. Sophia simply raised an eyebrow at her as Aunt Gertrude chastised her once again. "Oh Sophia, please forgive me. I seem to keep saying the wrong thing today. I believe I am so weary from the journey."

"Do not concern yourself. Yes, Viscount Rutherford was elderly, but he was a good match for me. He needed a young wife to give him an heir. It was not a bad marriage. He was kind and, in the evenings, he would tell me about his travels in India. It was fascinating. Perhaps one day I shall write down all his stories and put them in a book."

"Viscount Rutherford was quite the catch in his youth, you know," said Aunt Gertrude. "All the ladies wanted to dance with him at the *ton* balls. Of course, in the end, he only had eyes for poor Sarah. What a tragedy that was. I'm glad he found companionship with you, in the end, dear and I do wish he'd known that he had an heir."

"I like to think he does know, Lady Wardlaw."

"I'm sure he does. Now tell us how your brother fares."

Sophia sighed. "Sometimes I think he hears me and then I think it is probably just wishful thinking, but yesterday I clasped his hand and I was sure his fingers tightened around mine. I speak to him you know. It sounds silly of course. The apothecary told me he cannot hear a thing but I am not so sure."

"I am sure he can hear. I do not know anything about such things, Sophia, but it is worth speaking to him just in case."

"I have thought about sitting and reading to him. I wondered if I should read a book. He was reading Waverly by Walter Scott when he was hurt. I don't know if I should continue or read something else that he would already know by heart."

"What would he know by heart?"

"Parts of the Holy Bible I suppose."

Emily grimaced. "You want to bring him out of his sleep, Sophia, not put him deeper into it."

"Emily. I think it best you hold your tongue. You have now added blasphemy to your sin of rudeness this day."

Emily turned to her Aunt. "You cannot tell me you have not dozed off during the vicar's sermon, Aunt Gertrude. It is not the first time I have had to nudge you awake lest your snoring is noticed." Aunt Gertrude had the decency to turn a little pink at this.

"That is the vicar's words, not the word of God that causes me to fall asleep and don't be impertinent."

"Doesn't the word vicar mean that he is here in the stead of the Lord Jesus Christ? Surely you should be awake to hear his words also."

Emily knew she was being far too impertinent but she was always being chastised for speaking her mind and sometimes she could not help herself. She was chastised for being clumsy, for being too loud and for being disorganised. Her sewing box was messy and disorganised, her paints were messy, her brushes not properly cleaned. If it was not for the fact she had a maid, she hated to think what state her clothes would be in.

"Emily, would you come upstairs and see my brother?"

"Is that appropriate?" asked Aunt Gertrude.

"I shall be with Emily the entire time. It is completely appropriate since he is sleeping, probably dying. I shall not tell the *ton* if you do not, Lady Wardlaw." Sophia gave Aunt Gertrude a sweet smile and Aunt Gertrude resumed drinking her tea.

As they climbed the stairs Sophia spoke quietly. "I see you have not yet perfected the art of holding your tongue, Emily."

"Alas, I have not. I try very hard but it just comes out. I do not mean to be argumentative or inappropriate. I believe it is why I have not yet found a suitor. They think I'm gauche and ridiculous. I fear I shall never find a suitor and Robert shall be left with me to be the maiden aunt to his children."

"Do not give up hope yet. You may yet find someone who wants a young lady who is a little different from all the other simpering misses on the marriage mart. Anyway, here we are. This is Gideon's room."

They walked in and Emily was very aware that the room smelled like a sick room. The brown haired, handsome man was lying on his side, his eyes closed, his body unmoving.

"The apothecary told us to keep moving him onto his sides and back so he does not develop sores from being in one position. Apparently, even with a feather mattress, he is not immune to the ravages of lying in one position for three weeks. His poor valet is at his wit's end. He had been massaging oils into his limbs and his..." Sophia looked at Emily and blushed. "... his buttocks to keep the blood flowing. He says he has no idea if it does any good but he is hoping so."

However, Emily was aware of a smell in the room that was not the liniment or Lord Beattie's shaving soap. It was a slightly putrid smell. It was coming from the area around the bed.

"Did your brother sustain any wounds when he hurt his head, Sophia?" she asked.

"I don't believe so. His hand was bleeding a little. I think he caught it on a nail."

Emily moved to the bed and inspected one of Lord Beattie's hands. It was perfectly fine. But when she lifted the other, she could see the problem. His hand was now infected and yellow pus was dripping onto the bedsheet.

"Sophia, we need to attend to this before your brother ends up with a fever, if he does not have one already."

Sophia's eyes were wide with horror. Emily placed her hand on Lord Beattie's head. He was not warm. He was not particularly cold. She suspected he could do with another blanket.

"Ring for a maid, get soap and water and we shall clean it and find out how bad it is. Will your cook know how to make a poultice? I must confess I know they exist but I have no knowledge of how to make one."

"I'm sure she does." She walked over to the bell pull and rang. A few minutes later, a man appeared.

"Ah, Burke, we need very hot water, soap and some cloths. Lord Beattie's hand is infected."

"Of course, my lady." The man bowed and left.

"Who was that?"

"Lord Beattie's valet."

"You should dismiss him. How he could have missed this is beyond me. The smell is putrid and I noticed it as soon as I walked in."

"I didn't smell a thing. Though I must confess my sense of smell has been a bit odd since I started increasing. The strangest things make me want to cast up my accounts."

"You have an excuse. He is with your brother every day and for a large amount of the day. It is his job to ensure the welfare of Lord Beattie."

Sophia's eyes glistened and she lifted her hand to her mouth. At once Emily regretted her stern words. She lifted herself off the bed and hugged Sophia.

"I have let him down, have I not?" Sophia said against Emily's shoulder.

"Not at all. The wound is small. We should be able to draw out the poison. Do not upset yourself, Sophia, dear. It is not good for you or the baby."

Sophia managed to compose herself and when there was a slight tap on the door she was standing at the window gazing out over the parterre gardens discussing the dreadful weather. Emily could not help but smile to herself.

"Come," she called. The valet came in holding an ewer of hot water which steam was billowing out of and a cake of soap. He had a couple of towels over his arm.

"You said his hand is infected, my lady. Which one?"

Emily rolled her eyes. "His left one. The one that smells putrid, Mr Burke."

The valet's eyebrows raised in astonishment. "I was unaware of any smell. He had a cut on his hand but..."

Emily waved him away.

"My lady, I shall do it. He is my responsibility."

"No, Burke. I shall do it. Lady Rutherford's stomach is too weak given her condition and I want to make sure this is done properly." What in the devil's name was she saying? She had never done anything like this in her life, but she was so irritated with the valet, she was not going to allow him to touch that wound. She looked at Sophia, whose eyebrows nearly reached her hairline.

"Thinking of becoming an apothecary if your brother ever gambles away his vast fortune, are you, Emily?" she said, with a teasing smile.

"One never knows when a skill like this may be handy. Best to try on a sleeping patient first. Would you not agree?"

"Oh, I would indeed. Most definitely."

"I shall turn him onto his back then, my lady. If you wait on that side of the curtain."

"Really?"

"He is in his nightshirt, my lady."

Emily blushed. "Of course. I was not thinking." She turned to her friend who was hiding a smile behind her hand.

"Perhaps the weather will perk up now that you are here," Sophia said.

"I doubt I shall have any effect on the weather. It has been dismal since Christmas."

"What are they saying about it in London?"

"Oh, some are claiming that the four horsemen of the Apocalypse are due to arrive any day now, that Napoleon and all his armies were but a foretaste of what is to come. Not that most of them were anywhere near the war. The ladies flap their fans and weep over the hems of their gowns which are all ruined beyond repair and the gentlemen discuss how to keep their boots more watertight for longer. Of course, the newspapers discuss the riots over food, but there is still plenty of food to be had in town."

"That is good for those in town. Sadly, out here, it is becoming quite dire. I do worry what will happen if Gideon does not recover."

Emily laid a hand on her friend's arm. "I am sure he will."

"It has been three weeks, Emily. I do despair of him ever waking."

"Oh, Sophia, he is but a young man. Surely he shall recover."

"He was found under a large pile of debris with a large contusion on the back of his head. Who knows what damage has been done and if he will be in his right mind when he wakes. If he wakes. You hear of men coming home from the war with injuries to their minds and behaviour. What if Gideon is like those men."

"He has not been at war."

"But his injuries may be just as bad as if he was in the blast of a cannonball. Who can tell?"

"I have every faith he shall make a full recovery." Emily knew that she spoke from a position of ignorance. She knew nothing of the sort but she hoped fervently for her friend's sake that she spoke the truth.

"His lordship is ready, my lady," said Burke, appearing from the other side of the bed. "He is decent...or as decent as a gentleman can be when he is in repose."

"I promise you shall not be needed to fetch the smelling salts, Burke. I am not one of those ladies who swoons at the very thought of a gentleman removing his gloves."

Why she had said that, she had no clue. The most inappropriate things were just being blurted out of her mouth today. She did, however, always look at a man's hands when she met him. She was not sure why. Usually, they did wear gloves. One could tell a lot by the type of gloves a man wore. When he had no gloves on, by his fingers. She liked strong hands with well-manicured fingernails and slight signs of being weather-beaten, but not too much.

She moved around the bed and lifted the viscount's hand. It was perfect. She almost sighed with appreciation. Then she remembered that the other side of his hand had an infected wound. She shook her head. She was such a ninny.

She turned Lord Beattie's hand over and grimaced at the smell and at the pus that oozed from the wound.

"Are you sure you would not prefer me to do it, my lady," asked the valet.

Emily squared her shoulders and drew in a deep breath.

"No thank you, Burke. I am sure I am quite capable."

"Then may I suggest that you cover your gown with a linen first—to protect it from any dripping water."

"Oh, of course."

The valet held out a large linen, the size of which one would use after a bath. It was folded, she laid it gently on her lap, then she laid Lord Beattie's hand on the linen. He made no movement or noise. It was rather disconcerting to have a gentleman's hand so close to her and it not be scandalous. Though she supposed that she would have several Grande dames reaching for their smelling salts if they were to witness her behaviour now.

Burke had dipped a smaller linen cloth into the hot water and rubbed some soap onto it then he passed it to Emily. She gave him a tight smile before turning her attention to the viscount's hand. She was beginning to regret her impulsive decision to clean the wound.

"Are you sure he will not feel this?"

"I accidentally cut his chin while shaving him a week ago, my lady, and there was no reaction. I did not mean to, of course, but it is difficult when he is unable to hold his head still for me." Burke suddenly looked worried about his admission.

"Do not worry, Burke. I know it cannot be easy caring for a man who is perpetually in a state of sleep." Emily glanced up to see her friend move nearer to the bed while reassuring the valet.

"No, my lady. It is not. I am sorry about not noticing His Lordship's hand."

"No matter. Let us hope that no harm has been done. Lady Emily?"

Emily turned back to the task and swiped at the hand, cleaning away the pus and crusted blood. The smell worsened and made her stomach roil. Her mouth watered in the way one's mouth watered just before one cast up their accounts. She turned her head to the side, drew in a deep, calming breath and handed the cloth to Burke. He took a new cloth and handed her it. It was hot and soapy. She cleaned the hand again, working deep into the puncture wound.

"I think he hurt himself on a nail or a large splinter of wood," said Emily to no one in particular. If anything, she was really trying to keep her mind off the pus oozing from the wound and the blood now mixed in with it. Burke handed her another wet and soapy cloth.

"We must keep changing the cloths and we must get as much of the pus out as possible, my lady. I know it is not pleasant. I shall take over if it is too much for you."

"I can manage, Burke." She pressed harder and a little murmur escaped from the lips of her sleeping patient. Emily glanced at Sophia over her shoulder. Sophia gasped before she knelt on the bed and brushed her brother's hair from his forehead.

"Gideon, it is me, Sophia. Are you well? Oh well, of course, you are not well. You have not woken in three weeks, but this is the first sign of life from you in that time. Oh Gideon, please come back to us for I really do not know what will happen to me if you... if you..."

Emily turned to her friend but Sophia waved her hand in dismissal.

"Sophia?"

"I am well. Please, carry on cleaning the wound. It is better that the infection is removed than that you care for my silliness."

Emily swapped her linen again and pressed on the wound. It was now mostly blood that oozed from the puncture.

"I think we now need the poultice."

"I shall go and get it, my lady." Burke took the bowl, the dirty linens, except the one that Emily was holding against the bleeding wound and disappeared out of the room. Lord Beattie made another little moan and his fingers curled slightly against her hand.

"Sophia, his fingers moved."

"Oh my!" Sophia hurried around the bed and gazed at her brother's hand but it was still. Emily pressed slightly harder in the hope of eliciting more movement from the sleeping viscount but to no avail. Sophia's eyes clouded with disappointment. Her eyes shone with tears and she lifted her hand to her mouth.

"Oh Emily, do you think it is possible that he may get well. I cannot bear the thought that he might..." and then Sophia rushed from the room leaving Emily alone in a gentleman's bedchamber. With a gentleman. Albeit one who had not stirred for three weeks but it was still rather disconcerting and quite inappropriate. He moaned again. She sat down on the bed and swiped the hair back out of his eyes. It appeared he had a stray lock of hair that would not stay off his forehead.

Her gaze took in his features. A wide forehead with the beginnings of lines which were smoothed out in slumber, long eyelashes which grazed his cheeks. A strong jaw, a straight patrician nose and signs of a day beard.

A movement drew her eyes to his lips. Has he just licked his lips? Her gaze flicked up to his eyes and she could see there was movement underneath his lids. He was dreaming. She lifted to her feet and bent over him, her face very close to his.

"Gideon, can you hear me" It was not proper for her to call him by his given name, of course, when they had not been introduced, but these were extraordinary circumstances. She placed a palm against his cheek and his head moved slightly into the touch.

Emily remembered the book of fairy tales she had read as a child. One where a prince had fought through a forest and kissed a princess awake after one hundred years of sleep. She wondered if it would work. Of course, Lord Beattie had not fallen asleep because of a curse and he had not slept for a hundred years, but suddenly Emily very much wanted to press her lips to those of the sleeping viscount.

She looked furtively at the door, drew in a deep breath and pressed her lips to his.

Nothing.

She pulled away, slightly discouraged. Her first kiss had been... well... it had been disappointing, to say the least. Perhaps it was better if one's partner was awake. Surely it was better if the kissee was participating. Yes, that was it. It was only because Lord Beattie was asleep. His mouth had been dry and hard and not at all like the romance novels suggested.

She was saved from further musings by Sophia re-entering the room, handkerchief in hand, as she dabbed her eyes.

"I do apologise, Emily. I should not have left you alone. You should not have stayed. It is not appropriate for you to be in my brother's bedchamber alone."

"Only you know I was alone and as you can see, he has not ravished me."

Sophia chuckled. "You are far too improper for your own good. I am surprised no one in the *ton* has given you the cut direct yet."

"I am sure that day shall come. Especially since I shall soon be on the shelf."

"I do not believe you shall be. You just need to find a nice gentleman who suits you."

"Were you happy with Viscount Rutherford."

Sophia's smile was sad and wistful. "I was content. I knew we would not have a terribly long marriage as he was much older than me but Emily, we must take our happiness where we can find it."

"I think your brother is improving. I believe he was dreaming. His eyes were moving under his lids."

"They were? How interesting."

Just then Burke arrived with a muslin cloth filled with a noxious smelling substance.

"Milk, bread and camphor, to draw out the poison. I shall put it on."

He walked around the bed and it was the first time that Emily really took in the bedchamber. Masculine colours of dark turquoise, black and gold, with dark furniture. The gloom cast by the dark day did not lighten the room any but she suspected the room would be lovely on a nice day as the sun bounced off the gold on the wallpaper and the gilt around the coving.

"Come, we should get ready for dinner," Sophia said, breaking the spell of Emily's wool-gathering.

"Yes, we should."

"Then you should go to bed early. You have had an eventful few days, what with highwaymen and your first attempt at being an apothecary."

"I believe being an apothecary was more of a trial."

"At least the smell has gone. I did believe it was something to do with me increasing. Thank you for discovering the source of the smell. I do believe Gideon would have been very cross to wake up and find we'd had to have his hand cut off."

"Oh Sophia. I thought I was the young lady who was inappropriate."

"I am a widow, my dear. I am expected to be inappropriate."

Emily laughed as Sophia motioned her towards her guest quarters.

Chapter 4

His head was aching. Devil take it. He had no memory of last night. He must have been in his cups, and he needed to relieve himself, but oh, how his head ached.

He tried to open one eye but it seemed crusted shut with sleep. How awful, and his head. Had he drunk Brooks' out of wine and brandy? Good God. He would sleep a little more and then try to get up. No doubt Burke would be in soon, grumbling away and making a noise as he laid out his clothes.

He had vague memories of a dream. A kiss. Maybe it wasn't a dream. His hand was pained. Ah, his mind seemed to be too confused. Sleep was what he needed. He would never drink this much again.

∞ ∞ ∞

Emily had come upstairs to change. Having spilt her tea down the front of her dress, she needed to don a new day dress. They would not be going out that morning. It was far too wet—again. Emily was beginning to feel a little melancholic about the weather. Three days since they had arrived at Beattie Hall and they had been stuck in every day. Martha had checked her coiffure, nodded her approval and Emily hurried out of her room to go back downstairs to join her aunt and Sophia. The door was open as she passed Lord Beattie's room. She wondered how his hand had healed and if it was still infected.

Not that, that dolt of a valet would know. He had not noticed the first time.

She should leave it and go with Sophia to see the viscount, but what harm could it do to sneak in and check. He was still sleeping. Of course, it was entirely inappropriate, but this was the country. Only Sophia would know if she was caught and her aunt of course.

She checked left and right. There was no one else in the vicinity. A little check of his hand would do no harm.

She hurried around the bed and lifted his hand. It was still slightly red around the puncture wound. She thought it may need another poultice. She pressed her finger to the wound.

Lord Beattie moaned and moved his head slightly.

"My lord, do you feel that?" She pressed again and he moaned as his tongue came out to moisten his lips. When she pressed a third time he scrunched up his nose.

She glanced up at the door. She was no princess and he was no prince but it was now or never to see once and for all if the theory worked. She pressed her lips once more to his.

∞ ∞ ∞

What the devil was wrong with his hand and what was pressing on it. A searing pain was going through it.

""My lord, do you feel that?" Yes, he felt that. She sounded rather refined for a courtesan or maid. He didn't bed maids. She couldn't be a maid.

She pressed his hand again. Damn, it hurt.

Then her lips were on his. Her sweet lips. Well, they were pressed against his as if she did not know what she was doing. That was odd. His bladder was full and he had one hell of a cock stand. His mind was like wool. He lifted the hand she wasn't squeezing and tilted her head so he could kiss her properly. Ah, now she got it. Maybe it had just been the angle. Or maybe she had thought he was asleep and had not wanted to rouse him. Her lips were soft and she tasted of tea. He would love a cup of tea. When the tip of her tongue touched his, a little moan escaped her. He had just pushed his tongue past her teeth when he heard two intakes of breath—a male one and a female one. The woman he was kissing pulled away with a squeak of horror.

Gideon groaned and peeked one eye open. He appeared to be... in his father's room in Beattie Hall.

The courtesan... he peeked to the side and opened both eyes wide. She was a young lady in a day dress.

He turned his head slowly to see the village apothecary and Sophia. Sweet, beautiful... and pregnant Sophia.

"What....?"

Chapter 5

Aunt Gertrude sat on the window seat in Lord Beattie's bedroom. Burke had arrived with an invalid cup filled with tea. Lord Beattie was growling something about not being an invalid, despite his hand shaking. His lip had split and was now bleeding due to having been so dry.

"There is nothing else for it. You shall have to marry," said Lady Wardlaw, pulling out her fan from under her shawl and wafting it in front of her face. "Really Emily, what were you thinking?"

"I was not thinking, Aunt. I was merely acting on impulse."

"Oh!" More fan waving. "Dogs act on impulse, Emily. Young ladies have self-control."

"I do not believe we shall have to marry. Only Sophia and the apothecary saw."

"The apothecary cannot be trusted to hold his tongue, Emily," Sophia said. "He is also distantly related to the Earl of

Bachcomb who lives but ten miles from here. If the Earl and the Countess learn of this, then the rest of the *ton* will learn about it too."

"I thought you were supposed to be on my side, Soph." The viscount's voice was croaky but there was a glint of humour in his green gaze.

"I believe it is the best thing for you both." She glanced between Emily and Gideon. "Emily has a good dowry, she is a young lady of good *ton* and you do not believe in love matches. You should marry her to save her from scandal and to increase the wealth of the estate, which we both know Papa left somewhat depleted."

"*Sophia.* I told you that in strictest confidence."

"That is true, Gideon and I thought you could behave with a young lady, even if she was in your bedchamber. It appears we are both to find disappointment in this lifetime."

"She kissed me."

"You did not have to kiss her back. She is impulsive, silly and I love her like a sister. She needs to be protected. You are a peer of the realm, Gideon. For once in your spoilt, aristocratic life, stand up and do your duty."

Lord Beattie waved away his fussing valet as if brushing away an annoying fly and looked at the three ladies in his bedchamber.

"I do not wish to sound rude or impertinent, but I am somewhat befuddled. I feel like death, quite frankly, I have no idea what time of day it is, or even what day it is. I cannot remember what happened last evening and why I am even sleeping in a nightshirt, and what the devil happened to my hand? It hurts like the very devil. I assume I was in my cups."

All three ladies gasped, Sophia rounded the bed and took Gideon's wounded hand in hers. Only when he winced and pulled away did she seem to remember to be careful.

"Oh Gideon, you were not in your cups last evening. You have been asleep for three weeks. You were injured trying to mend the stalls in the stables. Part of them came crashing down about your ears and you were hit on the head."

"And Caesar?"

"Caesar?"

"My horse."

Sophia gaped. "How can you ask about your horse at a time like this?"

"Caesar is a brilliant piece of horseflesh. I adore that horse. Is he..."

Sophia rolled her eyes.

"He is very much alive and needs you to get better so you can take him for a decent ride. Your hand was injured and became infected. Luckily, Lady Emily noticed the smell and cleaned it out for you."

Emily could feel the heat rising in her cheeks as the viscount gave her an assessing look.

"Lady Emily, it appears you have very good medical skills."

"Thank you, my lord."

"And adequate kissing skills."

"Oh!" She turned away, her cheeks flaming.

"Gideon. That was very ungentlemanly of you." Sophia sounded angry. There was a slight thud. "Do not hit your head against the headboard."

"Please accept my apologies, Lady Emily. I am not myself. I cannot believe this is happening. You tell me I have just awoken from three weeks asleep and I must marry Lady Emily because she was kissing me. Pray tell, why were you kissing me?"

Emily closed her eyes and wished herself anywhere but this room.

"I thought it might make you wake up."

"Pardon? Why in the devil..."

He had obviously been stopped by his sister.

"Please explain, dear."

Emily drew in a deep breath. Oh, they would think her such a ninny.

"I know it is silly but I had this strange idea that if I kissed him, like the prince kissed the princess in the children's story, he might awaken."

"What a ridiculous idea," the viscount growled.

"You are awake, are you not?" Emily could not help herself. Of course, she felt foolish, but he had awoken and now she may have to marry the brute. Although, if marrying him meant kissing him again...

Emily shook her head. She was only fit for Bedlam with thoughts like these., and everyone was looking at her.

"There is nothing else for it, young man. You will marry her."

As she turned to her aunt, her gaze was arrested on the gentleman in the bed as he ran his hand through slightly long brown hair, his brows furrowed, his green eyes dark and brooding.

"Lady Wardlaw, I appreciate..."

"Don't try to charm your way out of this, young man. I remember seeing you with your nanny when you were in leading strings in Hyde Park. You will marry the girl and that will be an end to it."

Lord Beattie raised an eyebrow at Emily's tyrant of an aunt. His gaze then flitted to Emily and she wanted to squirm under his assessing gaze.

"She will need some help to be more ladylike if she is to be presented to society."

Emily gasped.

"I have been out in society for... well, this is my fifth season."

"Your fifth season and you are not wed yet. What is the matter with you?"

Emily swallowed as tears burned in the back of her eyes.

"I do not wish to marry and I will not marry."

She lifted her skirts and hurried out of the room. She did not go far, however. Instead, she stopped in the carpeted hallway and waited to listen to the conversation in the viscount's bedchamber.

"I apologise for my niece. She is impetuous but I shall convince her. She shall be ruined otherwise. Please Lord Beattie..."

"Lady Wardlaw, I implore you to stop. My head is pounding. I do also have to visit the necessary soon. We shall continue this discussion later. However, I do understand the need to marry. I also, begrudgingly agree with my sister. I also need to marry and if your niece has a good dowry then she is a suitable match. No doubt, I can keep her out of mischief."

"But she said she would not marry you."

"Lady Wardlaw. I am a consummate rake. I can charm the birds out of the trees. Your niece is child's play to me."

"That does not fill me with much comfort, Lord Beattie."

Lord Beattie chuckled. "If I were wed, Lady Wardlaw, I would be faithful to my wife. I take vows that I make in front of God very seriously, and I do not make a habit of debauching young ladies."

"Yet you were in the process of debauching my niece when the apothecary walked in."

"I was half asleep, Lady Wardlaw. I was not in my right mind. I had no idea who she was. She was kissing me and I was in bed. I assumed she was someone who had come there of her own free will and whom I had charmed or paid for her services in full knowledge of her circumstances. Had I known she was an innocent young lady of the *ton*, I would have..."

"You would have what, Lord Beattie?"

"I do not know, Lady Wardlaw. What I do know is I would not have continued to kiss her back. What kind of a gentleman do you take me for?"

"I do not know you well enough to form an opinion of you, Lord Beattie, though I have not heard any unfavourable gossip about you."

"That is because there is none for you to hear, Lady Wardlaw."

"You shall take care of my niece."

"I shall, and I shall organise a common license once I am fit and well. I should be well enough in a day or two."

"You have not eaten for three weeks, Lord Beattie. Give yourself some time. As long as she marries you, Emily's reputation is safe. I bid you farewell."

"Please, if I am not up and about tomorrow, will you chaperone Lady Emily to see me?"

Emily did not wait to hear her aunt's response. It appeared that everyone had decided her fate. She was to marry a man with whom she had barely exchanged a few words. A man who meant to charm her to his will. Well, she would not be charmed. She would not marry the brute. His kiss may have excited her but she would not give into the charms of a self-confessed rake. She would find another way out of her dilemma. She would remain in the country. A spinster, in a little cottage, with just a housekeeper and a maid.

Oh, but where would she keep her horse and carriage? Where would the coachman, the stable master and stable hand live? The gardener? What a terrible fix she was in. How did people survive in the country in just a little cottage?

She arrived at her room and hurried to the window seat. She curled her legs in front of her so that her gown covered her knees and ankles, she leaned her head against the cool panes. She watched as the droplets of rain trickled down. She had never felt so alone. No one understood her. No one tried to. She was a silly goose who was always getting things wrong, but she tried so hard to be a proper lady.

When Lord Beattie had asked why she had never married, it had been on the tip of her tongue to tell the truth. *For I am clumsy and awkward and sometimes say the wrong things in company. Especially when I am nervous.* But that would never do. What would he have thought of her? Of course, he would find out soon enough if he did marry her.

The idea both appalled and excited her in equal measure. Her only option was to stay away from the viscount as much as possible and then he could not possibly charm her.

What an excellent plan.

Chapter 6

"This is a dreadful idea, Aunt."

Gideon chuckled at the voice of his soon-to-be-intended outside his bedchamber door. She clearly had no idea how far her voice carried. He could not hear the reply of Lady Wardlaw who had obviously perfected the art of hushed tones.

He had insisted that his valet at least have him sitting in a chair for this meeting, even though he was in a dressing gown and had a blanket over his knees. He felt like an old man. That said, he also felt as weak as a kitten and it did not sit well with him.

"I shall not marry him and I do not want to visit him in his bedchamber. He shall not change my mind."

More hushed mutterings from the dowager viscountess.

"You should have refused on my behalf. I am Sophia's guest, not his."

Again, some murmurings.

"Yes, Aunt. It is his house but... oh very well. I cannot argue that point."

There was a quiet knock on the door and once he had bid them enter, Lady Wardlaw entered looking somewhat harassed. He did not blame her. This chit was going to be a trial. The chit entered behind. She was wearing a light blue day dress with a white shawl around her shoulders. Her hair, while pulled up into a pretty style, was damp and her cheeks ruddy.

"Good afternoon, ladies," he intoned.

Lady Emily looked like a skittish horse who wanted to bolt. Lady Wardlaw looked severe. He had arranged for tea to be brought up and a maid placed the tea tray in front of Lady Wardlaw.

"I should really have had the tea tray placed in front of you, Lady Emily since you will soon be the lady of the house."

"I..."

"Emily!"

Lady Emily looked at her aunt and turned a deep crimson colour, then concentrated on her hands in her lap which she began to twist nervously. She had obviously been about to refuse his suit.

"I do hate to be a burden, Lady Emily but would you mind passing me my tea," he asked. She looked up into his eyes and gave him a tremulous smile. Her blue gaze was wary but there was a keen intelligence there. "I am still quite weak from my enforced bed rest."

"Of course." She jumped to her feet. "What do you take."

"Milk and two sugars."

She added both and passed him the cup and saucer. The porcelain rattled as her hand shook. She then fixed her own cup before sitting down.

"I think we should get right to it," said Lady Wardlaw, but Gideon raised his hand surreptitiously, Lady Wardlaw saw his signal and gave him a knowing smile.

"You have misgivings about a match between us, I believe, Lady Emily."

"Who told you that?" Her pert little chin raised and she looked directly at her aunt.

"You did when you stomped out of here last evening. Or was it still afternoon at that point. No matter. And just now. Outside my door. You really must learn to use a softer tone if you want to keep secrets."

Emily bit her lip. He liked calling her Emily in his head, even if she had not yet given him leave to use her given name. She enthralled him. She was pretty enough. Not one of the beauties of the *ton*. He did not recall ever having met her at any of the social gatherings but then he avoided the most obvious entertainments of the marriage mart. At the balls he had to attend, he spent most of the evening in the card room and would dance, only when he felt he had to, usually with a friend of the family or with a distant cousin. Until now, he'd had no wish for a leg-shackle.

Her prettiness was understated. Her day gown was pleasing enough and hinted at full breasts. Her arms were slender which suggested her legs and waist would be slender too. Her face, while a deep shade of pink at present, was naturally like a peach and her blue gaze was guileless and innocent. Her long dark lashes brushed her cheeks and her tongue darted out to wet her rosebud lips. Damn, he wanted to kiss her again.

"As you see, my lord, I am really not a good match for a viscount."

"Oh, I am sorry, my lady."

She looked up at him, her brow furrowed in confusion. "Why are you sorry?"

"I apologise for the low status of my birth. Were you holding out for an earl? Or perhaps a marquis, or even a duke? I know you are the daughter of an earl so my lowly birth was probably not what you were hoping for in the least."

"N-no. It is not that."

"Oh, I see. It is like the children's story. You wanted a prince. I fear, the Prince Regent is already wed. Perhaps you are looking for a Prince from far-off lands."

She gazed at him, a mixture of horror and confusion marring her pretty features.

"My Lord, I..." But Gideon could not hide his smile any longer.

"Lady Emily, I am..."

"You are vexing me."

"A little. You look so serious. You are not here for me to pronounce judgement upon you. I only wanted to get to know you better. What activities do you enjoy?"

"I enjoy singing."

"You do? Who is your favourite composer?"

"Johann Sebastian Bach."

"Oh, I do love his music too. I enjoy Handel's music just as well. Do you play the pianoforte?"

She scrunched her dainty little nose. "Alas, I had ten thumbs when I tried to play the piano. I play the harp adequately. What activities do you enjoy?"

"Horse riding." Her eyes lit up at that. "I assume you like horse riding too."

"Of course."

"When I have my strength back, we shall go take the horses out. No doubt Sophia's mare could do with a good gallop."

"The ground is too wet to gallop."

"I know of a few places we may be able to get up a little speed."

"That would be nice."

"Shall we say in around three days?"

She looked at him sceptically.

"My lord..."

"Please, call me Gideon."

"Oh!" She bit her plump pink lip. God, it was adorable and it sent a spear of desire right through him.

"You do not wish to call me by my given name?"

"I... yes... but..."

"If you are not ready to give me leave to call you by your given name, then I can wait." He gave her his most dazzling smile. The one he knew could charm the garters off the least willing widow.

"I would like you to call me by my given name, Lord... I mean Gideon."

"It will be my pleasure, Emily," he said. He lifted his cup to his lips and raised an eyebrow at Lady Wardlaw. She gave him the slightest nod of appreciation.

He turned the discussion to weather and the gossip from town. Both ladies joined in and they spent an interesting half hour in one another's company. He found Emily to be a keen watcher of people. Her little asides showed an eye for details and curiosity about the people around her. He could tell she was used to being on the fringes of society, rather than in the heart of it, but it did not seem to perturb her in the least.

After tea, the ladies took their leave and Gideon was left to his thoughts. His thoughts turned to the young lady who would become his bride. What would it be like to bed her? He'd considered it a few times over the course of her visit to his bedchamber. The memory of their first kiss haunted him and he wanted a rematch. He had been wrong in his initial assessment of her. She was beautiful. It was just that he was not used to women who were not strutting in front of him like peacocks, trying to garner his attention. Her beauty was innate and masked by her lack of ambition to land a husband.

He imagined her naked on his bed, her long hair, cascading over the pillow, her breasts heaving in anticipation of their wedding night. Damn, he was getting aroused. Probably not a good idea, given his state of health. He hauled himself to his feet and hobbled to the window to look out on the waterlogged parterre gardens. Surely this weather couldn't last much longer.

Chapter 7

Sophia walked into his bedroom, Gideon placed his paper onto the bedcovers and looked at her.

"Should you be coming into my bedroom unaccompanied?"

Sophia's trill laughter rang out.

"You're my brother, you silly man. You're hardly going to ravish me."

"Hmm, that's true. Though, try telling George Byron that."

"She was his half-sister and anyway, I know you better than that."

"I should bloody well hope so."

"Stop swearing. I came to see how you are keeping. Is your hand any better?"

He lifted his hand, gazed at the puncture wound on the palm and flexed his fingers. There was still a little redness around the wound and it still hurt, but it did not pain him half as much as it had when he had woken up.

"It is fine. Are you well?"

"I am well. Blooming actually." She moved around the bed and as she walked, her gown tightened slightly around her bump. He worried for her.

"Do you think you are having a boy?"

She chuckled. "How would I know, Gideon. I am not a soothsayer."

"Some say women have a sixth sense about these things." She laid a hand lightly on her stomach and sighed.

"Part of me hopes for a boy as it was dear Octavius's greatest wish to pass the title onto a son, but part of me hopes for a little girl, who shall not have the burden of being a viscount from birth. Who shall not have people counting the months of my confinement to make sure she is legitimate. I... I am not sure that I trust Mr Benson, Octavius's nephew. He seems to want the title very badly indeed. He was rather distressed to hear that I was increasing and wrote to me demanding a letter from the apothecary confirming that I was with child."

"You have just received this letter."

"No. I did not tell you about it before because I did not want you riding off on your horse to put a bullet through his head."

"What makes you think I will not do that now, sister."

"You are still weak."

"Not so weak I cannot defend the honour of my only sister."

Sophia giggled. "Honestly Gideon, you are silly. You have to charm Lady Emily."

"Ah, but she is just Emily now."

"She allows you to address her by her given name?"

"I told you I was charming."

"Of that, I am in no doubt, Gideon, but Emily is not your usual lady."

"I am under no illusions on that score, Sophia. She is an enigma, but she is also beautiful, intelligent and charming in her own way.

"Oh!"

They both turned to find Emily standing in the doorway.

"Emily?" Sophia said.

"I apologise. Aunt Gertrude said I would find you here, Sophia."

"Do people not knock in Cumberland?" he asked, his eyebrow arched. Emily's cheeks turned dark pink. Dash it all, he loved making her blush. He could not wait until she was flushed and panting under him.

"Ignore my brother, Emily. He is a brute."

"But a charming brute. Emily, what say that this afternoon, I don some clothes and we take a turn about the garden."

Her eyes grew to the size of saucers. "But it is raining, my lord."

"Yes, it is, but it appears that if we wait until the rain ceases, we shall be in our dotage. I shall find an umbrella and you can raise your skirts so they don't trail in the mud."

"You are rather bossy, are you not, Gideon."

"I am, Emily. Get used to it. I shall be bossy when we are wed, and you shall enjoy it."

She glanced at Sophia and Gideon glanced at his sister too. Her eyes were lit with merriment and she sucked her lips into her mouth to stop herself from laughing. She knew he meant in the bedchamber, but Emily did not. Devil take it. When did his sister become so worldly wise? His gaze dropped briefly to her stomach and he felt a pang of regret for the young widow. Once her year of mourning was out of the way they would have to find her a new husband. She could not spend her life in isolation, whether the child was a viscount or the daughter of a viscount.

"I shall help you find something suitable to wear outside. If you have not brought anything warm enough, I am sure you can borrow something from me," said Sophia, hurrying to her friend and ushering her out of the door. "Behave, Gideon," she said, over her shoulder. He smirked but felt a warm feeling in his belly, just above his hardening cock.

Chapter 8

Gideon—she liked that name as it suited the rather austere but sometimes funny viscount—did not take her to wander through the parterre gardens in front of the house as she had imagined he would. Instead, he led her down a path towards a lake and some trees. He held an umbrella over her but he did not shelter under it himself. Instead, his hat and greatcoat were his defences against the unending drizzle.

She supposed the aspect would have been lovely any other year but nothing was growing and the grass was waterlogged. Some patches had now turned yellow because it had seen so little sun this year. It really was a very sorry sight. Emily knew most of England was in a similar state. She had heard from her brother and apparently Cumberland, Northumbria and Scotland were faring a little better. It was still colder and wetter than usual but partly because they grew hardier crops and partly because their weather had not been quite so miserable, they were looking forward to a harvest of some description.

"I received a letter this morning."

"A letter?"

"From your uncle. Lord Hargreaves."

"My mother's brother."

"Yes. He is good friends with the Earl of Bachcomb whom he is visiting. He wants to come and visit. The letter came from the Bachcomb estate. It appears he wants to slap a glove in my face for debauching his niece."

Emily suddenly felt very cold and very dizzy.

"No!"

"No? No, what?"

"He cannot. You did not."

"That matters not to hot-headed men defending the honour of their nieces, Emily. He says he will come next week on his way back to London. Beattie Hall is on the way."

"Next week? He is waiting a full week to defend my honour?"

Gideon huffed out a breath. "I'm rather pleased that he is waiting a week to defend your honour. It gives me another week without having my brains shot out."

"How horrible."

"The week or the brains."

"The brains."

"Hmm. You are rather hard to fathom at times, Emily."

"I do apologise."

"Please do not. I like it."

"We must do something."

"Yes, we must. Your uncle. Is he sane?"

"I believe so."

"Good."

"How far from the Scottish border is your brother's estate."

"Only a few miles."

"Fine. Pack your things tonight when you go to bed. Before dawn, I shall come and wake you. We shall elope to Scotland.

"Elope?"

"Yes, Emily. Elope. We shall marry in Scotland without the need of a licence. If you wish, we can collect your brother on the way to be our witness. Assuming he agrees to our marriage."

"I have not even agreed to marry you."

"For pity's sake woman. Your uncle thinks I defiled you. You have no choice. Half the *ton* will think you are a fallen woman by now."

"But..."

"But what?"

Emily could think of no arguments. Not any that would hold sway against this brute of a man who was glowering down at her.

"This was not how it was meant to be." Her voice sounded like a whine, even to her ears. Tears burned behind her eyes and her throat ached with the effort not to let them fall. She would not cry in front of Lord Beattie. He scowled at her for a moment then picked up her hand and laid it upon his sleeve.

"Come."

He was very brusque, she concluded, as he marched her around the trees and down a small path towards a summer house.

When they arrived at the large round glass house, he opened the door and ushered her inside. Some plants were dotted around the outside of the circular room but none had flowers. There were also wicker love seats, chairs set around the outside and a couple of tables. On a nice day, this would be a delightful place to have tea.

"This is a favourite haunt of the ladies during our annual garden party for the villagers. Alas, I fear there will be no garden party this year."

"Because of the weather?"

"Mostly. Also, because I have been unwell now for four weeks. Now we must make our way North to marry and find grain. I plan to ask your brother to help on that score. I could marry you here, Emily. It would make no real difference but the servants bring me tales of growing unrest every day. There is rioting in Wales. Do you know how close we are to the Welsh border?"

"I know Herefordshire is on the Welsh border but..."

"We are but three miles from the border. Offa's Dyke is on my land. That was the original border between the Welsh kingdom of Powys and the Anglian kingdom of Mercia. Emily, we are a day's ride from Hereford and if we are to go North to try to procure some grain, we do have to leave as soon as possible. Much though nothing would give me greater pleasure than to wait three weeks until the banns are read or to at least get a common licence from the bishop, I fear time is not on our side."

Emily looked down at her hands, trying to unravel the threads of Gideon's explanation. She was beginning to understand his haste.

"So, let me understand this. The people in Wales are rioting and since we are so near the border, you are concerned that unrest will leach over the border and affect your people."

"Yes. I fear it is beginning to already."

"And going to Hereford to see the bishop to get a common licence so you can marry me here will take time out of your journey North to get grain to hopefully resolve the situation here."

"It shall but..."

She held up a hand to stop him.

"But you must marry me soon because of the gossip and you do not need a licence in Scotland."

"We must save your reputation, Emily."

"And your skin, Gideon."

"I do not fear your uncle. I am told he is a poor shot."

"I fear you will grow to hate me because you were forced to marry someone to whom you are not even attracted, Gideon."

He took off his hat and dropped it on a table. Then he shucked out of his greatcoat and dropped it on a chair. He advanced on her and Emily was reminded of paintings she had seen in an art gallery in London of large cats stalking their prey. He tugged on the ribbon of her bonnet and tossed it onto another chair. Then he lifted her chin to his. His green eyes were dark like the colour of pine trees. He smelled of Sandalwood when he was so close. A lovely woodsy smell that made her almost lightheaded.

He cupped her cheek and tilted her chin so that she had to look him directly in the eye.

"Why would you think I do not find you attractive, Emily?"

"I... you..." She shrugged. She had not particularly thought on it. She had merely assumed. She was not well regarded by gentlemen of the *ton*, and her company was not sought after for dances or waltzes during the Season. She was just Emily. She was no great beauty. "I am just me."

"I like 'just you.' 'Just you' are charming and beautiful and unique."

"I am clumsy and awkward and not at all ladylike."

His gaze flicked down to where her décolletage would show, but for her pelisse covering it, and back up to her eyes. She was sure his breath hitched. "You are very much a lady, Emily. I think you underestimate your appeal."

Her mouth was suddenly very dry and she licked her bottom lip. A rumble, which sounded very much like a groan, came from the viscount's chest.

"My lord? Are you well?"

He closed his eyes as if reaching for his patience then opened them. Emily was all rather confused, but a little excited too. This was all far beyond her ken but Lord Beattie enthralled her like no other man ever had. Of course, she had seen very handsome gentlemen at Almack's, in the ballrooms of Mayfair and at the theatre but while she could appreciate their good looks and charm, she had never felt drawn to them as she did with Gideon. She had felt drawn to him even before he had awoken.

"I am well. Emily, have you ever been kissed?"

Heat flooded her cheeks. "I am not sure."

"You are not sure. Emily, it is a simple question. One usually knows if someone has planted their lips on one's own lips."

"Does kissing you in your bedchamber count?"

He frowned. "For argument's sake, let us say no."

"Then I have not."

"That kiss was your first kiss?"

"That would be correct."

"Then it is time for your second kiss."

"Oh!"

He smiled as he lowered his head and captured her lips gently with his. He encouraged her to open her lips and everything that she had started to learn in the bedchamber came flooding back. She lifted her hands onto his shoulders and pressed her body wantonly against his.

He angled his head, his tongue moving deeper into her mouth, exploring leisurely. He used one hand to undo the buttons of her pelisse and once the garment gaped, he moved his hand inside. It was then she realised he still had his gloves on. Emily pulled at his hair as sweet sensations travelled through her. Her nipples tightened and an ache settled between her legs. The viscount trailed little kisses along her jaw and down her neck as he cupped her breast with his hand. Suddenly Emily felt very vulnerable and pulled away.

"Please, my lord. Please stop."

Gideon froze and watched as she took two steps back from him and pulled her pelisse tight around her.

"What is the matter, Emily? Did you not like it? Was I too... rough?"

"I... yes. I liked it well enough." She did not want to sound wanton. In truth, she had liked it very much and she craved more. It was part of the reason she pulled away.

"Then I moved too quickly. I apologise. I should never have undone your pelisse and touched your breast."

Oh, how scandalous of him to mention her breast. She bit her lip and turned her head to look out of the summer house windows but they were all misted up.

"No. I liked it and I suppose I will have to get used to it if we are to wed."

"I would hope you would do more than get used to it, Emily. It should bring you pleasure."

The way his voice rasped out the word 'pleasure' sent a shiver through Emily.

"It does. It did, I mean. I am just unused to it. That is all. I am also concerned that I do not know what to do."

"To do?"

She gathered her courage and looked him in the eye.

"My mother died when I was twelve. I cannot possibly ask Aunt Gertrude to explain and I fear asking Sophia. I know she would explain but..."

"You do not want to appear silly in front of your friend?"

Emily shook her head.

"Well, there are two answers. Firstly, Sophia will not think you silly. My mother died in childbirth with Sophia so I do not know whom she asked about her wedding night. Perhaps she was as confused and apprehensive as you are, but worry not. I know what I am doing and I will guide you through it slowly. I understand that the first time may be painful for ladies but I shall do my best to be gentle."

"I have seen animals on the estate mating. Is it like that?" she asked.

His eyes crinkled with laughter and he chuckled.

"Not quite though the general idea is the same. The position is usually different. That said, once we are more practised, if you want to try that position, I would be more than willing."

"Positions?" She frowned at him and pursed her lips. Oh dear, it sounded very complicated indeed.

"I have confused you, have I not. It really is very simple, my dear. Worry not. Women have been doing this for thousands of years. It's easier than falling off a horse."

"Oh, I am an expert at that."

"Well then, I look forward to helping you become an expert in bed sports."

Emily was sure her cheeks must be aflame.

"Lord Beattie!"

He waved a hand dismissively. "Really Lady Emily, while perhaps I should moderate what I say, I see no reason when I am going to wed you in but one week. Take off your pelisse and gloves and come and sit with me."

He moved to a settee which looked rather narrow for Emily's liking. Emily was never one to shrink from a challenge. She removed her outdoor clothing. It was not as cold as she had imagined it would be. She walked over to him and sat beside him. His hands were also now bare, again she admired his strong hands and perfectly manicured nails.

"Do you mean to ravish me, Lord Beattie?" The words were out before she had a chance to stop them.

Gideon barked out a laugh.

"Ravish you? In a summer house. Good Lord, no!" He lifted one of her hands and pressed it to his lips. Emily sighed. The kiss sent tingles all down her arm.

"Is it very wanton to say I enjoyed your kiss?"

He smiled, a warm smile that reached his eyes. "It is not wanton at all, my lady as long as you only kiss me."

A smile tugged at her own lips and despite the slight chill, she felt warm inside. He bent his head and pressed his lips to hers. This time the kiss was sweet and his arms moved around her waist. She cupped his cheek with one hand and moved her other up his coat, enjoying the feel of the wool over his rippling chest muscles.

She opened her lips and his tongue began to explore. Her own tongue made tentative little forays into his mouth and he moaned appreciatively. Eventually, he pulled his lips from hers and placed his forehead on hers.

"Oh, my beautiful Emily. Seven days in a carriage with you will send me to Bedlam." Her hand was still on his cheek, he moved his head and captured her thumb in his mouth. Her finger was caught between his teeth but it did not hurt. Then he swirled his tongue around the pad and Emily's eyes widened. The ache between her legs turned to a throb. A little gasp escaped her and Gideon let her thumb go.

Neither said anything but Gideon gave her a knowing look. Did he know what effect his action had just had on her? But, of course, he did. He was a rake. He had admitted it himself to her aunt. Now she was his. He didn't seem so tame now he was no longer sleeping.

Chapter 9

Was he sure what he was doing? Devil take it. Of course, he was not sure this was the right course of action. Eloping with an innocent, dragging her to Scotland in the worst weather in known history. Trying to collect grain which would only put them at risk from highwaymen and robbers.

Would her family ever forgive him if Emily came to any harm? Would he forgive himself? His mind wandered back to the afternoon before in the summer house. She had been very unsure of herself, but a few times, she had lost herself to the pleasure and allowed him to lead her. Those had been the moments when he had nearly forgotten he was kissing an innocent—when he nearly took things further than he ought.

He would have to be careful.

He placed the book he was reading onto the table and stood. It was time to waken Emily. A few servants were awake, but only a couple whom he trusted to keep their mouths shut until the time was appropriate. They needed time to get away.

He walked as quietly as possible upstairs and along to Emily's bedchamber. Of course, this was terribly improper, as was eloping but there was nothing else for it.

He cracked open the door and there she lay, atop her covers, dressed and ready to go. Her boots lay at the bottom of her bed and her pelisse and fur shawl were thrown over a chair, her bonnet on the dressing table beside them, but she was fast asleep.

Gideon chuckled. He approached her and as he leaned over to shake her, he could not prevent his impulsive action. He pressed his lips to hers.

She muttered something and moved her head slightly but he kissed her again. This time, her eyes fluttered open. Recognition brightened her gaze and her tongue shot out to moisten her lips.

"Gideon?"

"Yes. It is me. It is time to go."

"Now?"

"Yes now." God's teeth this woman was going to be difficult. She didn't ever just obey. He wanted to kiss her more. That slight brush of the lips had whetted his appetite. He was annoyed at himself. He should be more in control. Why did she get under his skin so?

She had scurried out of bed and was putting on her pelisse.

"Whatever will people think of me? Running away like a thief in the night." She sounded upset.

She swirled her long braid into a knot and began to jab pins into her head. Gideon winced but Emily did not seem to notice. "They will think I am with child or something equally disgusting."

Gideon moved over to her and stilled her hands. "Being with child is not disgusting. It is the beginning of a new life and something wonderful. The people who matter will know you cannot possibly be with child. You and I know the truth. The rest of the *ton* can go and hang themselves for all I care what they think. When no baby arrives in seven months, they will know that you were not with child. Now stop rambling as I have no wish to have to double back to Bedlam to leave you there. It will add a week onto my journey at least."

"You would not."

"I would if you continue to rave like a mad woman."

She glared at him and he chuckled and pressed a kiss to her nose. "I cannot tell when you jest and when you are serious, my lord."

"That pleases me. I should like it to remain so. That way, I shall have you dancing on your toes throughout our marriage. Now, boots on and we shall go to the kitchen. Mrs Harrower has made some tea and pastries and I want you to have a glass of brandy before we go to warm you inside. Denholm has placed a couple of hot bricks for our feet on the floor of the carriage. Your bag is already in the carriage. I thought since we are travelling light and the weather so bad we would take our valises into the carriage with us."

Emily nodded and put on her boots.

Half an hour later they were trundling down the private road and out of Beattie Park estate. His plan was to either borrow a coach from Emily's brother, hire or buy one in Carlisle if necessary. He hoped Emily's brother would be willing to loan them one. That way he could bring grain home for his people with the minimum of cost.

Emily was sitting with her back ram-rod straight as though she were sitting in the Duchess of Wellington's drawing room during afternoon tea. She could not sit like this for an entire carriage ride. She would be in agony by the end of it. His carriage was large enough and well sprung. He had considered selling it along with some of the horses which had been in the other stables when he'd had his accident. Why he hadn't put Caesar in with the other horses, he didn't really know. He had been stupid and pig-headed.

He leaned on the sill of the window and placed his chin on his hand, considering her for a moment before speaking.

"I do not plan to ravish you, Emily. There is no need to be on your guard."

Her head whipped towards him and her lips thinned. "I am not on my guard."

"You are clutching your reticule like a weapon, you are sitting with your back as straight as a soldier's and you have a look of grim determination on your face. If the wind changes, as my nurse used to say, you will remain that way."

Her shoulders sagged slightly and she released an audible sigh.

"I did not sleep much. What time did you waken me?"

"Half past four."

"I heard the clock chime four."

"So, you only got about twenty minutes of sleep."

"Perhaps less."

"I too did not sleep." He pulled a blanket from the seat opposite them and spread it over their legs. Then he pulled the ribbon of her bonnet and tossed it onto the opposite seat along with his hat. When he placed his arm around her, she stiffened momentarily but he crooned to her the way he crooned to Caesar when he was skittish.

She slowly relaxed under his gentle hold and sank against his side. He brushed his lips against the top of her hair. Already she felt so comfortable—so right. As if she belonged there.

She nuzzled into his coat and he settled back properly on the seat. He wanted to fall asleep but his mind was racing. He'd left instructions for his man of business, letters for Sophia, Emily's aunt and he trusted his staff implicitly. He was slightly concerned about Sophia. He didn't trust her late husband's nephew and just hoped the dire weather would keep the foppish little squirt from coming anywhere near Herefordshire anytime in the next three weeks. That said, he did have a few footmen who were handy with their fists if Sophia was in danger and he was the local magistrate.

Edwin would be put behind bars until Gideon returned in three weeks if he tried anything and the village prison was no picnic.

"Are you sleeping, Gideon?" Emily asked about an hour later. He had been dozing fitfully in between his musings about his sister.

"Hmm, not really."

"Neither, am I?"

"Oh, that must have been the coachman I heard snoring," he said, grinning.

"I do not snore."

"You do a little but it is delightful ladylike snores." She moved her hand and he was painfully aware that her arm brushed over his hard length. He'd been half-asleep with a beautiful woman who smelled of lavender and lilies in his arms. He had not paid any attention to his body's reactions to her.

She stilled and raised curious eyes to him.

"Is that...?" She moved her arm until it was her hand touching him through the buckskin of his breeches. He stifled a groan.

"My...uh... manhood, yes."

She spanned it with her hand. It was just about the same length. She raised her hand towards her face and her mouth dropped open. The absurdity of the situation made him guffaw.

She was the most hilarious creature he had ever met. He adored her.

"I... That is not possible." She frowned and moved away from him.

"What is not possible?"

"I have seen statues in art galleries my lord. I am not so innocent that I have not seen statues."

He chuckled. "First of all, those statues are, um... how shall I put it? They are not aroused. They have not been in a rocking carriage with a beautiful woman in their arms who smells divine." She huffed out a breath and eyed the now uncovered placket of his breeches warily. "Secondly, they always sculpted those poor fellows extremely under-endowed. Perhaps the sculptors were trying to impress by making their own look bigger. Who can tell."

She was shaking her head, her eyes wide, her chin bobbing as she swallowed.

"We cannot marry, my lord."

"Why ever not?"

"My lord, I may be innocent but I grew up on a country estate. The bulls and cows do not care if a curious young girl watches them mating. I understand the general..." she waved her hands about as if trying to find the right words. "That will not fit inside me."

She placed her hand on her heaving chest and swallowed hard. How could he reassure her? She looked like she was about to open the carriage door and flee.

"Emily, did you ever see any of the baby animals being born?"

"Yes." She frowned, looking at him warily as if he was possibly fit for Bedlam.

"That's the same opening that is used for mating. The one the calf or piglet or the lamb comes out. Or in a human's case, the one the baby comes out."

She nodded. He had a feeling Emily had suspected this but not fully worked it out. "The opening stretches. You will be able to accept me into your body. And Emily..." He waited until she met his gaze. She was biting her lip and her cheeks were tinged a delicate shade of pink. "You shall enjoy it immensely. As I said, the first time may be painful but after that, you should find as much pleasure from the act as I do."

She looked down at her hands and he waited. He needed to give her time to compose her thoughts, he decided.

"Do you think me terribly foolish?"

"Why would I think you foolish?"

"I feel foolish because I do not understand what happens between wives and husbands, and your... manhood. It frightens me a little."

"I think you are exceedingly brave to be so honest about something which few ladies would discuss with their fiancé, Emily, but I am pleased to be able to put your mind at ease. We have a long journey ahead of us, and I would hate for you to spend it worrying about our wedding night."

"You say I shall like it after the first time."

"If you do not, then it is my fault and I am a terrible lover, but I have had no complaints before."

It was almost as if he could see his words settle on her and, as she made sense of them, the little green monster of jealousy rose within her. Her chin jutted forward ever so slightly and she lifted her head.

"I am sure you have not, my lord."

Damn. That had been crass.

"I apologise, Emily."

"No need to apologise. Men have needs. I understand."

He tugged her against him and kissed her temple.

"Come, let us sleep some more. There is another hour until we stop for breakfast. Do not be vexed with me."

"I am not vexed with you."

"It is a sin to tell untruths, Emily."

"It is also a sin to run off with men in their carriages, my lord."

"If you can find me the verse in the Bible where it says that, I will buy you a new ball gown."

"Now you are vexing me, my lord."

"You are vexing me as you refuse to call me Gideon."

"Yes, I am, my lord."

He chuckled as he pressed his lips to her temple.

Chapter 10

Although she had slept for a large part of the day, Emily felt exhausted when they stopped at the inn for the evening. There were still plenty of daylight hours left but the horses were wet, tired and the coachman was not at all happy about pushing them any farther that day. Gideon had agreed, deciding that on such a long journey, it was better to proceed with caution, especially given the state of the roads.

They had taken a few long breaks at coaching inns, giving the horses long breaks and Gideon was pleased with their progress. This was a small, not very popular coaching inn and Gideon had told the innkeeper they were called Mr and Mrs Smith. Emily could not help but think he lacked originality.

He had managed to organise a pair of rooms for them and some beds in the servants' quarters for the coachman and their stable hand. Their rooms adjoined each other with a connecting door.

The innkeeper led them first to Emily's room and gave her the key. He then led Gideon a little farther down the hall to his own room. Emily was no stranger to such establishments but she had never been alone in one with a gentleman.

She laid her valise on the bed and sat at the dressing table inspecting her appearance in the looking glass. She was rather bedraggled looking. Her hair was sticking out from the pins she had jabbed into it this morning at all sorts of angles, it was damp in some places and dry in others. Her cheeks looked terribly flushed and her pelisse was all crumpled. There would be a maid who could press it, she was sure.

A light knock on the connecting door made her jump. She closed her eyes and wished-for patience.

"Come," she answered.

He stood there in the doorway, his jacket off, his shirt sleeves rolled up and his hair slightly mussed from his hat. How could he still look so handsome when she looked like she had been dragged through a hedge by wild horses?

"I have organised a private parlour for our dinner, a maid to help you to bed and to help you dress in the morning. She can help you with any clothing you need to have pressed or cleaned."

"Thank you."

"I apologise. This cannot be comfortable for you."

"It is fine. I am used to inns. You cannot travel to London every Season from Cumberland and not use inns."

"Do you need the maid to style your hair before dinner?" She did. It was in a terrible state. She hesitated, not wanting to be a burden. "I can see that you want to say yes. I will arrange it for you. Never be afraid to ask for something. I have money. Things are a little tighter than I would like but I do have coin."

"Thank you."

He scowled at her pelisse. "Are you planning on going for a walk?"

"No."

"A carriage ride?"

"No."

"Why are you still wearing your pelisse?"

"I had not got around to removing it yet."

"Please, let me assist you."

He moved behind her and she undid the buttons. As his large hands slipped under the material and met the bare skin that her carriage dress did not cover, she shivered. He placed the pelisse over the chair then took her by the shoulders and pulled her back flush against his front. He snaked his arms around her waist and lowered his chin to her shoulder. She could feel the rasp of his day beard on her bare skin. Emily held back a shudder of anticipation.

"My lord?"

"Everyone in this inn thinks we are married." His soft, wet lips nuzzled her neck for a moment.

"Forgive me, Emily. Your head has been lying on my chest all day. I just want a moment to savour my fiancée." Without knowing what she was doing she moved her hands behind them both to his backside and urged him harder against her back. The thick rod of his manhood dug into the small of her back and he groaned as he sucked the lobe of her ear into his mouth and bit gently.

"Gideon,"

"Emily." He breathed deeply and then sighed. "I fear moving. If I move I have to let you go, or else I shall start to kiss you. If I start to kiss you I shall not stop. I need you but... I know I must wait. I know it is the gentlemanly thing to do, even if we will be wed in a few days' time."

Emily's heart was racing. "Is it very bad if I want you to kiss me?"

"No." His voice was rough and Emily was sure he was only just hanging on to his control. "But I need you to know I did not whisk you away from your aunt just so I could ravish you. Do you understand."

"I know. You are concerned about your people. You need to go up to Cumberland."

"I do, but a marriage should be based on more than just sex."

Emily burned with embarrassment at the mention of the word *sex*. It was such a common word.

"I see."

"Do you? We should have companionship, friendship and admiration."

"Do these things not need to grow."

He chuckled. "Well, my love, something grows quite easily when you're around."

Emily had no idea what he meant until he thrust his hips slightly and his manhood prodded her harder in the back. Was he talking about that? It grew when he was ready to consummate?

"Oh."

"Oh indeed. Perhaps we should find something to do before our evening meal."

He let her go and she heaved a sigh of relief.

"You could order tea and then you could read to me. I have brought my embroidery."

"How terribly stimulating."

She glanced out at the weather outside. "Well, you could teach me boxing, I suppose."

He let out a bark of laughter and her gaze met his.

"I did bring a deck of cards. Perhaps later we could play *vingt-et-un*," he said.

"Ooh, can we play for money?"

"Money? What sort of young lady plays for money."

"The sort of young lady whose betrothed would never come to collect his debts."

"Oh, I always collect my debts, Lady Emily. I may just take payment in kind." He wiggled his eyebrows almost imperceptibly but she felt the heat in her belly anyway.

"I...I...do not know what you mean." Her gaze met his and she could see the moment he read the fib in her eyes. The corners of his mouth lifted into a cat-like smile.

"I am sure an innocent young lady like yourself does not, but fear not, *my lady*, you will gain as much pleasure from my winnings as I shall."

What was it about the way he said the word *pleasure* that made her almost crumble to the floor with watery knees?

He strode to the bell pull and Emily wondered what he was doing. When a maid came, he ordered tea, her mind began to clear. Oh yes. Tea. That would give her some sense of normalcy.

"My Lord, the things you say to me... they are not proper."

He chuckled.

"I should apologise Emily but a day in a carriage with you clinging to my side has almost made me fit for Bedlam. I..." His mouth twisted as if he was choosing his words carefully. "I agreed to marry you out of duty. I could see you were pretty enough, had good breeding and although sometimes..."

"Clumsy, outspoken and a little bit airheaded?" she offered.

"You are far from airheaded. You seem very intelligent, and I like outspoken. Yes, you are outspoken. You do sometimes act without thinking, or else we would not be in this situation. I have not noticed you particularly clumsy."

"Oh, you will."

He waved it away. "Nevertheless, I have grown to have a high regard for you. When I kissed you in the summer house I realised I was extremely attracted to you., and that attraction is growing all the time. This enforced time together in the carriage shall be difficult if this keeps getting more intense. If I am crass, it is because I cannot let it out in other ways. It is because I cannot take you to bed and show you what I wish to do to you. Perhaps before our meal, when the maid is doing your hair, I shall go down to the taproom and have an ale with the men. Some bawdy discussion may help."

"I was intrigued by you when you were asleep. You looked so peaceful. Your valet had not noticed your hand was dreadfully infected. Honestly, Gideon, the man is a terrible valet." Gideon waved off her concerns. "Well, then I thought you were a brute. As high handed as my aunt. Demanding that I marry you. Then demanding that we elope. I do understand why we must and I do understand that it is my fault. I feel like such a ninny. When you talk about pleasure and the consummation of our marriage vows, I feel even more of a ninny. I do not understand most of what you say. You talk of... *it* growing?" She waved her hands in despair. "If it grows any more, I shall break apart. You tell me it will be fine but...but...but..." She was struggling to breathe. Had Martha tied her stays too tight? She wanted to cast up her accounts and swoon all at the same time. And she was not the type of lady who swooned.

He took her hands and crouched slightly so he could look into her eyes.

"Breathe slowly, Emily. You will have a fit of the vapours if you are not careful. All is well."

"It is fine for you to say all is well. You have not been spirited away to have some enormous pole pushed into your body."

He began to laugh and pulled her into his arms. She struggled for a moment then realised his hold was too tight. Besides, she found comfort from the shaking of his large frame.

"It does not get any larger than it was when you measured it against your hand in the carriage. It does get smaller when I am not aroused by the scent of you, by your nearness, by the very thought of you. My dearest Emily, women have been having sex with gentlemen for centuries and none of them has come to any harm. Child bed may be another matter but that's the cycle of life, unfortunately." He sounded sober now and his laughter had stopped. Yes, child bed was no laughing matter. It was dangerous, but so was riding in a carriage, walking downstairs and crossing a busy street. "Please Emily, do not fret about our wedding night. I shall make it as pleasurable for you as possible. Despite what you may have thought of me at first, I am not a brute. I shall take care of you."

She wrapped her arms around his waist and held tight. "I know you are not a brute. You have been very kind and nothing but a gentleman. These are not ideal circumstances. I do apologise that you have ended up having to marry me because of my foolish behaviour."

"I had to marry anyway. My parents had a love match I am told, but I have little regard for such things. I am a practical man. My father had many flights of fancy and he died a poor man. Luckily for us, I had my own investments so we are not poor. I shall be happy to be content. I am attracted to you, you are a young lady of good *ton*, and I believe we shall deal well together. You amuse me and I believe I shall keep you on your toes."

She pulled back and regarded him for a moment. He cocked his head in question.

"The gentlemen I have encountered are generally one of two types, the ones who have enough money that they do not need a young lady's dowry and so put off getting a 'leg-shackle' as long as they can. Usually, as long as they can avoid their own mamas in ballrooms and before their mamas become more cunning than they. Then there are those who need a dowry and will fawn all over any young lady who has a decent enough one. I have been the object of affection for one or two of those gentlemen but Robert or Aunt Gertrude usually steered me away. Which was just as well really. Poetry written out of desperation for money really is rather awful."

"Wait, the gentleman wrote poetry?"

"Two did, and let me tell you, Lord Byron may have left the country under a cloud of scandal which I cannot quite fathom, but at least he could actually write poetry. I do wish someone would explain what happened with Lord Byron though."

"I promise you, Emily, my dear. When you are no longer an innocent, I shall explain to you why Lord Byron had to leave the country."

"You shall?"

Emily knew no one who understood the scandal of Lord Byron—at least, no one who was willing to admit it.

"Only if you promise not to breathe a word to anyone. Especially not to any unmarried ladies."

"I promise." She may enjoy being a married lady after all if she was privy to all the salacious gossip of the *ton.* She hadn't considered that.

"Emily, you really are a little gossip," he teased.

She giggled just as the maid knocked and brought in the tea.

Chapter 11

Emily had been rather quiet at dinner. He had talked about his childhood a little and asked her about hers in Cumberland, but she had not been terribly forthcoming. She did mention her brother a lot as if she felt his childhood was more important than her own. That saddened him a little.

He had asked what she liked to read and for a moment her face had lit up as she'd admitted that she loved reading. When he'd asked what books she enjoyed, she had looked down and said quietly, "Oh, nothing of much interest, my lord."

His heart had wrenched for her. One minute the chit was confident and gregarious, the next, she was a little mouse, denying herself and being critical almost of her own existence. He remembered her description of herself as clumsy. He had not noticed her being clumsy particularly, but he had not spent much time in her company.

They finished their meal and were climbing the small narrow staircase, Emily just two steps ahead of him when she missed her footing and fell onto her hands."

"Ooft! Oh, devil take it." He doubted he had ever heard a young lady use such a curse, but he recovered. Moved up beside her and helped her. She was already halfway back to her feet.

"My lady, are you well?"

"I am fine. I apologise for my foul language, my lord. I told you I was clumsy. I did not tell you I swore like the coal man."

He chuckled. Then he realised her pert little bottom was pressed against his groin. His thumb was pressed just under her breast. How did he manage to get into such a mess? Or was it a mess? It felt dashed lovely to him. Experimentally he brushed his thumb across the underside of her breast. His cock started to harden.

"My lord." There was little censure in her words. There was definitely a lot of pleasure. He brushed his lips softly against her neck then let her go. She appeared to be gripping the bannister tighter than before.

"Go, before I forget myself and where we are."

Emily climbed the stairs and hurried to their rooms. He had the keys, he unlocked her door and followed her inside. Planning to go to his room via the connecting door. But he had to make sure she was well.

"Let me check your hands."

"My hands are fine."

"Please, Emily."

She sighed and held out her palms. They were a little red but they seemed unharmed. He lifted first one to his lips and kissed it, then the other. Her little surprised gasps sent need straight to his semi-hard length. If he was not careful, he would end up bedding her tonight. That was not the plan. She deserved better.

He dropped her hands and took a step away.

"I shall go and collect the cards from my valise, you ring for tea."

"Yes, my lord."

He brought back the box of cards and a book. He laid the book on a small table and put another small table between them. When the tea tray arrived, Emily poured them both a cup, added milk and sugar to both. It felt so domestic, Gideon could not help thinking that he would enjoy evenings together with his wife. Of course, the myriad of entertainments available during the Season may be exciting, but tea, and conversation with his wife, before taking her up to bed and sinking himself into her sweet body was the sort of life a man actually dreamed of.

"My lord?"

"Hmm? I mean, pardon?"

"Another card please." He passed her a five of clubs." Her smile of satisfaction proved her to be a terrible card player. He had eighteen. The chances of him winning this hand were pretty slim. She either had twenty, or more likely, considering her smile, twenty-one.

He laid his hand down to show her his. She triumphantly laid her hand down. He looked at the cards.

"That's twenty-two."

She looked at the cards, he brow furrowed.

"No, it's n.... Oh!"

He pursed his lips in an effort not to laugh. She shook her head.

"It happens all the time in the gaming halls."

"No doubt by men who are utterly foxed. What is my excuse?"

"You are likely tired. It has been a long day."

"I slept a long time in the carriage."

"Sleeping in a carriage is not as restful as sleeping in a bed. Come, stop chastising yourself for a simple mistake."

"I am such a ninny."

"Stop calling yourself that."

"I feel like an imbecile."

"You are not an imbecile because you miscounted some card, Emily."

She stood up and walked to the window. The night was beginning to fall, she wrapped her shawl tightly around herself.

He walked to stand behind her.

"Why did I never notice you at balls or entertainments in town?"

"Because I am not a great beauty, my lord."

"You are beautiful, but it is not how you look that stopped me noticing you. I notice most young ladies in a ballroom. Usually, of course, except those who do not wish to be noticed."

"I do not know what you mean, my lord."

"You sat among the wallflowers, did you not?"

She hugged her shawl tighter.

"I sat with a few friends. I do not care for dancing, my lord."

"You do not care for it or..." He left the question hanging.

"I told you I was clumsy. In my first season, I had a reputation for standing on all the gentlemen's toes."

"Ah!"

"I should have told you before we eloped. I will be required to host balls in your townhouse, shall I not?"

"My townhouse is not large, my lady. We do not host balls there. Sometimes we do have a little dancing. When we go to balls, you will dance with me and you can step on my toes as much as you like."

"You may not say that when they are blue and purple with bruises and do not fit into your fine hessian boots."

"Then I shall stay home until they are better. It shall be worth it. I can lie abed and perhaps you can lie abed with me. There is plenty to do in bed once we are married." Her breath hitched and since darkness was almost complete outside, the candlelight caught her reflection in the window. He could see the redness in her cheeks. "I meant reading. I could read to you. The works of Byron, or Mansfield Park."

"Oh, I plan to read Mansfield Park soon. When we next go to London, I shall get it from the circulating library."

"I'll buy you a subscription at a subscription library," he offered. She turned, her eyes lighting up.

"You would do that?"

"Of course." He knew a subscription was slightly more expensive but really, to him it was pennies. He did not understand why she did not already have a subscription. Perhaps her brother was not as well off as he led everyone to believe. He knew the Earl of Whitsnow to nod to in the House of Lords or in White's on the odd occasion someone took him there, but no more than that. Gideon's club was Brooks', so he was seldom in White's. They did not have the same friends and they did not share the same interests. Whitsnow was a dour chap and altogether far too brooding for Gideon. Of course, the fellow had become an earl at the tender age of sixteen and was two years older than Gideon. This meant that there must be four years between Whitsnow and Emily. But there had been no rumours of financial troubles for the Whitsnow estates. There were usually rumours if one was a gambler or bad with investments. Of course, people had not told him of his father's plight because... well, no one gossips to the kin of the subject of the gossip, far less the heir apparent.

He walked over to the table and picked up the book he had brought into her bedchamber earlier. He moved back quickly and presented it to her. "There is no need to borrow this one from the subscription library, however. It is part of our library."

She ran her fingers over the gilt letters on the spine of the book and her eyebrows raised, her brow crinkling comically.

"Mansfield Park?"

"I bought it last time I was in Town. Sophia has already read it, I brought this and my own book along for the journey. I was not sure if you would think to bring a book to read."

"I did not."

"Then, if this is the sort of book you may be interested in, you are welcome to read it as we travel north."

Her face lit up with excitement for a moment and then fell. "Thank you, but I shall be fine."

"You said you wanted to read this, Emily."

She gave a small deprecating laugh. "I do, but I would hate to damage your copy."

He frowned. "Do you make a habit of damaging books."

Her chin jutted out. "Not on purpose."

"Accidents happen. If it gets damaged, it gets damaged."

"I would prefer not, if it is all the same to you, my lord. Now I think it is time for bed."

She walked over to the bell pull, rang for the maid to come and help her get ready for bed. He had been dismissed. She had damned well treated him like a servant.

"As you wish, my lady. We will rise early tomorrow so that we can take it slowly for the horses."

"I bid you goodnight."

He bent and pressed a kiss to her cheek. The discussion about the book was not over but he knew when to retreat and regroup.

Chapter 12

Just for a change, it was raining when they awoke. Emily had dressed, with the help of a maid who had styled her hair simply but prettily. Too bad she would spend most of the day in a carriage with a gentleman who was likely not pleased with her. She had dismissed him last night rather abruptly because she was embarrassed. Robert would never allow her to borrow his books which was why he had organised her a membership of the circulating libraries both in the country and in town. She was just too clumsy and he would not have her damaging his books. He also bought her the cheaper membership of circulating libraries because they were cheaper and the books were usually already slightly damaged.

They had been quiet at breakfast, Emily allowing Gideon to read the newspaper which was one day out of date. They were in a private parlour and she mused about how she could entertain herself on the long journey. She had finished the book she had been reading on the way to Beattie Park and had not brought another book with her. It had been a book which she had saved up and purchased herself. She had read it four times but never tired of it. Oh, how she would love to read Mansfield Park. No matter. She would not ruin Gideon's books.

They climbed into the carriage and settled down, Gideon helping her off with her bonnet and him removing his hat. He tossed both on the seat in front and dug under the blanket that was sitting next to their valises.

He produced two books. He laid one on his own lap and handed her the copy of Mansfield Park he had shown her the previous night.

"Your book, my lady."

She looked at it and then out of the carriage window.

"I would prefer not to read, my lord."

He sighed audibly.

"I do not understand. You have professed a desire to read this book. I have a copy. Soon all my books shall be your books too, once we are wed. It is a long journey to Cumberland, I am happy to talk and play cards but even that, after a while, shall become mundane."

"My company is mundane, my lord?"

He raised an eyebrow. "I did not say that, Emily, and you know it."

"If I damage the book..."

"Then nothing terrible shall happen. The book shall be damaged. I shall either purchase a new copy or if it is not so badly damaged that it can go back in the library, then that is what shall happen. It is only a book."

"But books are expensive."

"They are meant to be read. If I thought you would wilfully damage a book then I would reconsider allowing you to read my books, but your concern about damaging them probably makes it more likely to happen. If I am not concerned, it may lead to you being less... concerned about damaging it. Please, read it and enjoy it."

He was so kind. Not at all like Robert. Oh, she loved her brother but he was such a dry old stick.

"I... thank you," she said, as she capitulated and accepted the book. His grin was huge and he lifted his own book. "Is this how our marriage is to be?" she asked.

"Sitting reading in a carriage in the rain. God, I hope not."

"I meant me having to follow all of your orders."

He pursed his lips and considered her. "Come now, Emily. You enjoyed our sparring. You were almost as aroused as I was."

"A-a-... I apologise, my lord. What did you say?"

He chuckled. "You heard, my lady. Suddenly you have a hearing impediment and you have become coy."

She opened her book and pretended to be engrossed looking at the title page.

He leaned close.

"I find that a book holds much more enjoyment for me if I hold it the correct way up, my lady." His breath tickled her ear and caused her to shiver involuntarily. She snapped the volume shut, turned to him but his lips, so close to hers entranced her and his piercing green eyes were hooded and seductive. "Tell me you were not aroused when you argued with me."

"I would not even know what aroused meant, my lord."

"Excited, scintillated, wanting more, a heightened state of desire."

"Desire for what?"

"It matters not for now, you desire me, do you not?" He lifted his hand and cupped her chin, stroking her cheek. She leaned into the touch. "You desire my touch."

She nodded and he pressed his lips to hers for a few moments then pulled away.

"I cannot wait to feel your touch on me, but for now, I shall have to make do with Patronage by Maria Edgeworth."

"Oh, I should like to read that book too. Do you have all four volumes?"

"I do though I only brought the first two with me. Once you have finished Mansfield Park, you are more than welcome to read it."

She sat back and opened her book, satisfied and happy. He looked at her for a long moment before turning to his book.

∞ ∞ ∞

It had been a dashed long day. The roads were muddy and the travel had been slow. They had not wanted to push the horses hard so Gideon had told the coachman just to keep the pace steady. He was happy to make as many stops as necessary, but he had to keep his cattle fit.

Now she slept in the room adjoining his and he was sure he could smell her on his shirt. It was keeping him awake, and hard as a rock. He could take himself in hand and relieve the tension, he supposed but he did not like doing that with Emily just on the other side of the door.

A loud rumble of thunder made him jump. He'd been aware that the rain was particularly heavy but he'd not seen lightning. Just then his room lit up for a second and then the eerie light was gone again. A squeal from next door made him sit bolt upright.

When no more noise came from the room adjacent, Gideon relaxed. Maybe Emily had a bad dream and had settled down again. Another deafening thunder crack brought a high pitched keening sound from the other side of the door. Not caring that he was only in his shirt, which hung low enough to cover the important parts, Gideon opened the door and was at the side of her bed.

"Emily, my love, are you well."

She had started to turn to face him and her face lit up with another flash of lightning. Terror etched her features and she curled into a ball with a little squeal.

"The storm," she managed. "I... I..." This time when her wide eyes poked out from beneath the covers they were wide and pleading. "I hate storms. I was caught out in one when I was a child. I... my horse... she died..." She sniffed. "I'm so afraid, Gideon. I always am. I used to climb into bed with Robert when I was a child, but now I climb in with Aunt Gertrude."

More thunder, she squeaked and curled up under the covers. Devil take it. He could not leave her, petrified and cowering. Against his better judgement, he pulled aside the covers and encouraged her to move over. She did not protest. Instead, as soon as he lay down, she wrapped her arm around his waist and buried her head into his chest.

His shirt had ridden up as he had settled. His arse was bare, as was a more pertinent part of his anatomy. He could only pray that her hand did not go wandering.

As another clap of thunder shattered the silence, Emily moved with a whimper. She began to climb up his body, her leg curling around his, her arm moving over his shoulder as her other arm burrowed under his body. Was she trying to send him to Bedlam?

"Lay still, my love, all is well." As lightning lit up the room again, she tightened her grip with her leg and started to rock against his thigh. He dropped his hand to her bottom. Powerless to do anything but encourage her, he moved his leg slightly and rocked his own hips. His hard cock was throbbing, but she continued to rub herself against him and he did not care.

"Gideon?"

"Shh, Emily. All is well."

"I feel..."

"Excited? Stimulated?"

"Yes."

"That is how you should feel."

"Is this...appropriate?" Now she was asking? He smiled closing his eyes and relishing the feel of her in case his answer put an end to their little interlude.

"No, but then neither is eloping and it has not stopped either of us from doing it. I shall not ruin you tonight, my love, but I can show you pleasure."

He tipped her chin and took her mouth in a searing kiss. She responded immediately, both in the thrusts of her hips and by kissing him back. Her moan of desire sent a spear of need through him. He would not take his own pleasure now. He was aware of the storm still raging outside but Emily seemed to have forgotten and was completely absorbed in what was going on in the bed. Their tongues danced and their teeth clashed as they tried to consume each other.

He'd had many women, but somehow this innocent creature was pulling more passion and desire from him than the most practised courtesan. She was finding her pleasure through sheer instinct.

Her lack of practised seductive techniques was more enticing and driving him towards the edge of his sanity.

When he moved his free hand up to her breast and brushed his thumb across her nipple, she gasped into the kiss. Oh, she liked that. He would enjoy doing that to her, regularly. Her breasts were soft and full and seemed to be very sensitive.

Suddenly it was no longer enough to allow her to find her own release against his thigh, He eased her onto her back and unwrapped her arm from his neck. When he broke their kiss, she made a little noise of protest.

"Open your legs to me, love."

"Gideon..." her voice trembled with nerves.

"I promise you, just pleasure. Let me touch you. Drop your knees to the side." He pressed his lips to hers and she complied. He pulled up her nightgown the final few inches, uncovering her nest of curls which, as his fingers brushed towards the bottom, proved to be already damp. As he moved his fingers through her folds, he was delighted to find her already wet as she writhed into his touch.

"So... perfect... so.... wet!" he punctuated each word with a kiss to her jawline.

"Wet? That is good?" she enquired.

"Very good." She was rutting against his fingers and he was massaging her pearl with tiny deft strokes. Her quick breathing and the grip she now had on the bedsheet told him she was close to release. He moved his head to her breast and sucked her nipple through the cotton of her nightgown. Of course, he could have stripped her but although this act was completely inappropriate, somehow it felt less so if he did not see her naked body. She would be pleasured and hopefully sleep through the rest of the storm.

"Gideon, please…"

He flicked his tongue hard over the distended nub of her nipple, making up for the reduced sensitivity through the wet cotton as his thumb worked the bud at the apex of her thighs, harder and quicker. She was moaning now with every thrust and Gideon was biting his lower lip. He was so hard and pained, but watching her strive for her own release was a pleasure in itself.

When she splintered suddenly, she cried out his name, reaching her hand into his hair and grabbing it, hauling his head to her mouth for a hard and bruising kiss as she thrust against his fingers to ride out her release. For an innocent, she was not slow to demand what she required at the height of her pleasure.

Gideon was pleased with this knowledge. It would mean that once she was more confident and informed, she would be an excellent bed partner. She jerked slightly against his ministrations and he revelled in the sensations he was still pulling from her. She was over sensitised. He would sell his soul to plunge into her warm, willing body right now. That said, were he to do just that he would probably lose his soul because he had promised her he would not. And he was an honourable man.

His aching cock-stand would survive another night of unsated lust. His honour would never survive not just disappointing Emily, but losing her trust completely.

"Oh my," she gasped. "It is no wonder no one explains what happens in the bedchamber before marriage or no young lady would ever make it to her wedding day a virgin." Her arm flailed onto the pillow beside her head. He wished he had lit a candle before climbing into bed. He would love to see her face properly now, flushed and bright. With one last swipe through her folds to gather some of her nectar, he raised his fingers to his mouth and sucked.

"Gideon," she wailed.

"Yes, my love?" He was enjoying himself.

"Your fingers. They were just on my... my..."

"On your...?"

Her lips thinned and her brows knit together. "You would make me say it, my lord?"

"I was merely interested to know what word or phrase gently-bred young ladies of the *ton* use for their most intimate area."

"That would have been how I would have described it. Why? What would you have said?"

"I would have used that exact phrase to you, my love."

"And among your gentlemen friends or to yourself?"

"I would not sully your dainty little ears with such words, my lady."

He continued to lick her juices from his fingers and thumb. She tasted divine. Emily wrinkled her nose.

"You should not do that, my lord."

"It is delicious. I cannot wait until I can spread your legs apart, put my head between your thighs and lick you. He opened his index and middle finger slightly and ran his tongue up the middle. Her jaw dropped. The little whimper she made sounded less than human.

"You would do that?"

"With pleasure and I believe you would enjoy it."

She frowned then pulled herself into a sitting position. "And what about you?"

"What about me?"

"What have I to do to you?"

"Whatever you wish."

She shook her head.

"That is not an adequate answer, my lord. You use your mouth down there," she waved in the general direction of her hips, then gestured to his. "Do I use my mouth down there."

God, yes.

"If you wish. If you do not wish to, I shall not force you."

"But, my lord..."

"Emily, come and lie down. You will end up in a fit of the vapours."

"I want to be a good wife," she said quietly.

"You shall be. Devil take it, woman. It has taken every ounce of willpower not to make you mine tonight. For I promised you that, but you were so responsive and I ached to do it. You were perfect."

"I wish you had made me yours."

"I promised I would not and it would have been dishonourable to go back on my word. Now, go to sleep. You must be tired now."

"Will you stay with me until the storm has passed?"

"I thought you had forgotten about the storm."

"No, but it does not frighten me as much with you here."

He snuggled her pert little bottom against his hard, aching cock and somehow, he did not mind that the storm still raging inside his body would likely not abate until long after the one outside had. His woman was content and already her breathing was slowing.

Chapter 13

"You were gone when I awoke this morning," Emily said as he lifted the previous day's paper and scanned the front page.

"Yes, I was." He did not sound like he was in the mood to talk.

"I thought you would stay until I woke."

"I had something to do." He sounded off-hand as if he was trying to avoid the subject.

"Oh."

He laid the paper down and lifted his cup to his lips. She admired his crisp white cravat, so neatly tied, even without his valet.

"We should be going soon. The weather is at least dry today. Of course, the roads will still be like a mire but at least the horses shall not get wet. They may not tire so easily."

"Of course. I...umm... I knocked on your door when I awoke. I could hear you in your room but you did not answer."

"I was busy."

"So busy you could not even answer?"

"Yes, Emily. God dammit. Instead of waking you and pre-empting our wedding vows I removed myself from your bed. I was dealing with the problem when you knocked. Please just let me be. I'm trying to be honourable."

Emily was confused. He wanted to pre-empt their wedding vows. Well, she did understand that meant bedding her before the wedding—and not just what they had done the night before. What problem was he dealing with? He wanted her to leave him alone. What did he mean by that? Tears sprung to her eyes.

"Are you abandoning me here, my lord? Last night... I was a loose woman. You are displeased with me."

Gideon's brows knit together.

"No, Emily. No. That is not it, and, of course, I would never abandon you. What sort of scoundrel do you take me for?" He was on his feet and pulling her up and into his embrace in an instant. "I was merely making sure I would be less... aroused in your company. I apologise for sounding annoyed with you. I find your directness a little disconcerting at times."

"My apologies, my lord. I shall try to do better. This morning when I woke up I thought you had perhaps realised your mistake."

"There has been no mistake, my lady. I would recreate last night every single night if I could. Now, finish your breakfast before I end up kissing you."

"That would be terrible, my lord."

"It would be if a maid walked in and I had my hand up your skirts."

Heat flooded her cheeks and she pulled away from him and sat down before pouring herself another cup of tea. When she chanced a glance over at Gideon, He was smiling as he read the newspaper.

∞ ∞ ∞

They had no longer settled in the carriage and the damned woman was demanding answers. Gideon was truly delighted with her, but he needed her to be his wife. He needed her to be less innocent so that when she was inquisitive he could explain things properly. He hated trying to dance around the subject matter in deference to her maidenly sensibilities.

"You said you would explain what you were doing when you would not answer me this morning," she began as soon as the carriage was trundling along the road. He closed his eyes and placed his head against the squabs. "Gideon?"

He pulled her onto his lap, her facing side on and she made a startled yelping sound but he covered it with his mouth. She melted into the kiss easily enough and soon he had the buttons of her pelisse undone. His hands roamed her body before he stopped kissing her mouth, pressed his lips down the column of the throat and onto her décolletage. He pressed dainty kisses just above the neckline of her gown. Of course, he was torturing himself as much as he was torturing Emily.

He pushed a hand up her skirt and onto her thigh. It took almighty willpower not to push her legs apart and move his hands farther up to find his treasure, but his plan was to explain this to her.

"How do you feel?" he asked at last.

"Feel?"

"Yes. How does your body feel?" He barely recognised the roughness of his own voice.

She scowled. "All... tense, I suppose. As if I want to burst. I want to rub myself against you. Oh, that makes no sense."

"It makes perfect sense. You are aroused. Men feel similarly, but we get hard too." He took her hand and pressed it to the fall of his breeches. Her fingers curled slightly around it and he groaned. He allowed himself a moment to rest his forehead in the crook of her neck and shoulder, just enjoy the feel of her hand around his shaft. Then he lifted her hand away and kissed her palm. "Sometimes the tension becomes unbearable and I feel the need to release it. Obviously when in polite company I cannot. It is like all urges, hunger, thirst, the need to visit the necessary. It can be controlled and it does go away, but eventually, it needs to be satiated. You were sated last night. I was not, so when I woke and was hard, I went into my room to resolve the problem."

"How?"

He pressed a kiss to her lips until she opened for him and his tongue danced off hers for a brief moment. "So dashed curious," he murmured against her lips. He pulled back and considered how to explain. "Well, I stroked you between your legs until I released the tension in your body. I did the same to myself. I stroked my... shaft until I released the tension in my body."

She licked her lips and Gideon closed his eyes. He did not need his mind going down that path right now. "You could not have done it last night?"

He shrugged. "I could have, but I did not want to confuse matters and it seemed ungentlemanly to take my own pleasure after having found so much pleasure in watching you."

She sighed and leaned her temple against his forehead. "I would not have minded."

"Perhaps not but I wanted you to sleep so you were properly rested."

They sat for long moments as she seemed to be contemplating the view out of the carriage window. Gideon ran his hands up and down her leg, toying with the bow of her garter ribbon. It should be erotic but it was actually soothing.

"Part of me thinks I should feel shame for what happened last night. I am not married and yet I let you touch me in the most intimate of places. I let you share a bed with me and now I sit on your lap like a courtesan."

"You are no courtesan," he growled. How dare she compare herself to a prostitute just because she had deigned to experience pleasure the previous night and was enjoying his touch now. They were to all intents and purposes married. The only reason they were not yet married was that Scotland was so damned far away and the weather was so atrocious.

"No, I am not but it is still the case that my behaviour is not becoming of an innocent."

"You shall not be an innocent for long, my lady. As soon as I have you over that border, you shall be my viscountess and you shall have my name. I apologise if anything I have done has made you feel uncomfortable."

"No, please do not say that. I did not finish my thought. Part of me thinks that, and part of me is enjoying the new experiences and looks forward with anticipation to all the other things you have to teach me."

"I did not think I would ever enjoy being a young lady's governess, my lady, but I shall enjoy instructing you."

This time it was she who captured his mouth in a kiss. A quick study indeed. Before the exchange could get any more heated, he moved her from his lap. He had to remain sane and he would not do that if the luscious creature continued to sit on his lap. Carriages were just not made for deflowering innocent young ladies—even if they did seem quite eager.

∞ ∞ ∞

Two days after Lord Beattie had explained to Emily what he had been doing in his own bedchamber in the inn the morning after the storm, she was beginning to feel, well, *frustrated* was the only word she could think to use. He had given her the odd peck on the lips, but nothing more. He had been the perfect gentleman. Of course, they were still four days away from Scotland assuming everything went well, and today was Sunday.

If truth be told, Emily had not been entirely happy with the idea of travelling on a Sunday but she had already eloped, shared a bed with a man before her wedding. Let him touch her *there*, and so how much worse was travelling after they had been to church? The Viscount promised her that not travelling on a Sunday was a man-made rule rather than a rule from God. He had said Jesus would get annoyed at Pharisees who tried to stick to the rules so strictly, that there was no room for manoeuvre in emergency situations like now.

When she had inquired how he knew so much, he had explained that he had originally been studying theology at Oxford, but when his older brother died of a fever, he'd had to give up his plans of becoming a vicar and change the subjects he was reading at university.

She had not realised he'd had an older brother, but then, she was not like some of the young ladies of the *ton*, who had Debrett's memorised.

They had spent their evenings playing cards, their days in the carriage reading and having the odd conversation. Emily very much wanted to invite him back into her bed but she could not very well do that now, could she?

She gazed out the window at the landscape. It seemed to be miles and miles of country all around. She needed to visit the necessary.

"Do you know how far it is until we reach the next inn?"

He did not look up from his book. "No."

"Would you mind asking the coachman to stop at the next inn if we are not stopping to rest the horses?"

He looked up this time and removed his spectacles to look at her. He only wore them when reading. "Are you well."

"Quite well. I need to... ahem..."

"Oh, I see. Do you have your courses?"

She was aghast.

"No."

"How urgently do you need to stop?" She grimaced as the carriage jostled over a rut in the road. "I see."

He pulled down the window and called to the coachman.

"Denholm," he called."

"Aye, milord."

"How far to the next inn."

"Three, maybe four mile, milord."

"Damn. If you find a clump of trees, and a place to pull in, just do it."

"Aye, milord."

"In the trees?" Emily squeaked.

"You can wet the seat if you like," Gideon said. "But it will start to smell after a few hours. However, in the trees, I shall be with you to make sure you come to no harm from bandits and the trees will cover you against peeping toms."

"I do not want you seeing me."

He rolled his eyes. "Really Emily. It is a natural bodily function. I may take the opportunity myself once we are out of the carriage. We are also going to be man and wife soon."

"For all the good that has done me these past two nights," she muttered.

"What the devil, is that supposed to mean?"

Had he heard her? Oh dear. He had been right about her voice being too loud.

Luckily the coach was slowing and pulling in to the side of the road, there seemed to be a veritable forest on their left-hand side. As soon as the stable hand let down the step, Emily climbed out of the carriage and was hurrying into the woods.

"Emily come back." She wondered why Gideon was so tardy but she would not look back. She was not waiting around for him—brute that he was. She weaved her way for a hundred yards or so until it started to get very gloomy and a little eerie. There was no rain now, just the odd big plop of rainwater which had gathered as it made its way through the large canopy of green leaves. She shivered.

"Bloody woman. You should have waited for me. I needed to get my pistol. You do not know who or what you shall meet in these woods. He tucked his pistol into the back of his breeches and grabbed her by both arms, pulling her against his broad chest. "You are a stubborn woman, Lady Emily.

"And you are a brute, Lord Beattie."

"You didn't think me a brute when you reached the pinnacle of pleasure the night of the storm."

She opened her mouth to speak but he took advantage and pressed his mouth to hers. It wasn't the brutal kiss she might have expected when he was angry with her. Instead, it was coaxing, teasing, playful.

"Never think I do not want you because I am honouring you, my lady. Damn, kissing you was a bad idea when I was planning to pay a visit myself. Be good now and go behind that bush and do what you have to do."

She nodded dumbly. Kissing her was a bad idea? How debasing.

She hurried around the bush and found a decent place to lift her skirts and squat. It was terribly unladylike but she'd done this a few times when she had been out on walks and been caught short. Gideon seemed to be muttering to himself for a moment or two and possibly pacing. A couple of twigs snapped behind her which she was sure was him.

Once she was finished she rounded the other side of the bush. He appeared to be standing to look at a tree. She walked nearer to look at his face and glanced down. Oh of course. She had seen her brother when he was young going against trees and walls.

How foolish. Gideon scowled at her. He looked ferocious.

Her cheeks blazed as she hurried away. How utterly mortifying. She broke into a run. She must have looked so priggish, just standing there looking at him emptying his bladder. She would never be able to look him in the eye again, never mind marry him. What must he think of her? Why could she never get anything right?

She was vaguely aware of him calling her name but she did not stop. She kept running. Running away from the absolute humiliation of having to see him again. Not that she had a plan. She never had a plan. Her breaths were coming in heaving gasps.

Then she broke through the trees. She did not see the root of the bush sticking up at the edge of the road. Her foot caught in it and she was heading downwards before she could even scream.

A shout rent the air, the splash of horse's hooves and carriage wheels through the mud made her freeze. It was too late. It could not stop in time. It was far too close and gaining on her. Gideon, Robert, Aunt Gertrude, Sophia, Gideon, all flashed through her mind. She was going to die.

Chapter 14

Suddenly she was flying, rolling backwards into the mud, a heavy weight rolling on top of her and then rolling off her, then on top of her again, settling there and pushing what little breath she had out of her.

"Are you hurt?" the voice asked through rasping breaths. "Emily, are you hurt."

She fluttered her eyelids and tried to work out if she was hurt. A little winded perhaps. Her ankle ached, and there was a dead weight on top of her.

"I..."

"Emily, are you hurt?"

She recognised the voice now. It was Viscount Beattie. Gideon.

"Gideon, you're crushing me."

He rolled off her.

"Are you hurt?"

She considered all the parts of her body. "My ankle is painful, but I feel no other pain."

He heaved a deep sigh.

"Milord. I saw what happened. Are you both well?" She looked up to find Denholm and the stable hand standing there, both wringing their hands.

"I think we are both well, though Lady Emily may have hurt her ankle. We shall get in the carriage and look at it. Can you help me up and then I shall carry Lady Emily back to the carriage?"

"Of course, milord."

Gideon glanced down her body and must have assured himself she was properly covered before he lifted his hand to his coachman. He was on his feet in seconds.

He was covered in mud. It was then she realised she was lying in water. Most likely very dirty water. She lifted her hand and saw mud covering her.

"Oh no."

Gideon ran his hand through his hair before bending down and placing a hand under her shoulders.

"You were nearly killed under the wheels of a carriage, Emily. A little mud is a minor detail at this point. Put your arms around my neck."

He lifted her as though she weighed no more than a feather. As they walked back, Gideon asked the coachman about the coach that had nearly run over Emily.

"Never really saw it, milord. Seemed to slow a bit but then carried on. I think it had a ducal crest on it. Looked fancy anyhow."

"It was my fault," said Emily.

"Immaterial. He should have slowed down to check you were alive or dead."

"Would one not know?"

"Not with the ruts on these roads, milady. Beggin' your pardon."

Gideon sighed.

"Denholm, go ahead to the coach and lay the blankets on the seats. We're both filthy and I don't want to dirty the seats which we still have to sit on for days."

"Aye, milord."

He hurried on and Gideon slowed his pace.

"I apologise for Denholm's crassness. He's not used to speaking more than the odd few words to ladies. He forgets about your delicate sensibilities."

"It is fine. I am fine." She pulled at her skirt and circled her ankle. "I think my ankle may be unhurt. It was caught in a root but I think I may just have turned it slightly."

"I shall stand you up when we get to the carriage and you can try it out."

He was tense, and it wasn't from carrying her. She could see the hard set of his jaw and the steely determination of his green eyes—as though he was reining in his temper. Was he angry at her?

Well, of course he was angry. She had been a stupid, stupid girl. She had nearly got herself killed. That carriage had nearly run her over, Gideon had saved her, and in the nick of time.

Suddenly she felt cold and she leaned against him—against his warmth.

They were at the carriage now and Gideon was lowering her to her feet. She immediately bore all her weight on her good foot, then tentatively, very tentatively, she stepped onto her foot that had been caught in the bush root. There was a slight twinge of pain, but in all honesty, she had felt much worse when she was a child.

"Well?" Gideon was frowning with concern.

"It is a little tender but I think it shall be fine."

"Hmm, I think we should wait and see what it is like in a few hours and if it swells. Then we shall decide if we need a doctor or an apothecary. Right, into the carriage." He handed her up, with less courtesy than he usually bestowed upon her. In fact, he practically hoisted her into the conveyance and bumbled in behind her, slamming the door. As soon as the rocking of the carriage stopped, signalling that the coachman and stable hand were in their places, Gideon rapped on the ceiling.

Gideon dropped his head back against the blanket covered squabs and wiped his eyes with his thumb and forefinger.

Emily looked down at her un-gloved hands. She was no lady. No hat, no gloves, covered in mud, having practically given her innocence to him, asking him about intimate things that men did, watching him relieve himself.

A big fat teardrop hit her hand and she swallowed hard. He must be regretting bringing her along. He should have left her to her ruination back in Herefordshire.

"Why in the devil's name did you run like that, Emily?"

"I...I...I'm so sorry."

"For what? For nearly killing yourself? God dammit, Emily. You nearly died."

"Maybe it would be better for everyone if I had."

"Why? Is the sight of me emptying my bladder so abhorrent to you? If it is, my darling, the marriage bed is going to be a bit of a shock."

"No-o-o!" She wailed. He did not understand. She did not even understand herself. She hauled in a deep breath and tried to control herself. She was being ridiculous, and now she was shivering. She lifted a hand to wipe her tears. She really was going to make the worst viscountess. Suddenly she was enveloped in both the blanket and his arms. She was trapped in a warm cocoon against his strong, virile body. "I apologise. I am not normally such a watering pot. The journey and all the experiences of the past week or so have made me quite emotional. I may have...over-reacted."

"Hmm, go on."

"I came around the bush after—well my own ablutions, shall we say and it did not occur to me what you were doing, even though as a child I saw Robert going against trees and walls, sometimes he was having a competition with himself to see how high he could get it to go." Gideon chuckled and she felt slightly better. "I thought you were just inspecting the tree. Had maybe found something interesting, holes from an iron ball from a pistol or something. Then I saw you had your... you had it out and you were relieving yourself. You scowled at me. I felt such a ninny, just staring at you. I was mortified."

"I was scowling because I was getting ready to reach for my pistol. I was not convinced it was you. While I would have preferred for you not to have witnessed me relieving myself against a tree, I am not such a delicate flower that I should wilt at the thought, and I believe you are not either. You are a ninny for running and not stopping when I called you back. I should tan your hide for that."

"You would hit me." She tried to pull away from him but he held her tight.

"No. I would never hit a woman, tempted though I may be in this instance for your damned stupidity, but, my darling, you need to start thinking before you act and before you speak. Kissing sleeping viscounts in their bedrooms, running away from absolutely nothing and nearly getting yourself killed, blurting out the first thing that comes into your head. You truly are a master of disaster. Or a mistress at least."

She gave him a rueful smile then bit her lip. "Are you very disappointed that you decided to marry me?"

He pressed his lips to her temple. "No, not at all. I think life with you shall at least never be dull. I would soon have had to start looking for a wife in the ballrooms of London and no doubt I would have found some primped and perfect young lady just out of the schoolroom. Who would have said just the right thing at all the correct times and would have produced the perfect heir and spare, but I may very well have died of boredom before I was in my fortieth year."

"You may have been better just spending more time in your box at Drury Lane if you wanted to be entertained than marrying me, my lord."

"Mayhap, but the theatre makes me an observer, not a participant in all the goings-on. While I do not wish to have to save your life every day, as these wet breeches are deuced uncomfortable, I shall enjoy being part of your madcap entertainments."

"I am sorry I got you wet and muddy and thank you for saving me."

"Speaking of wet and muddy..." he leaned over and closed the curtains over the carriage windows then did the same on the other side. He then half stood and lit the lamp inside the carriage.

"What are you doing?"

"It is still quite a distance to the next inn and we do not know if they shall have rooms ready. We shall have to change in the carriage."

Change? In the carriage? In front of him? Emily eased out of Gideon's hold and pushed herself as far into the corner of the seat as she could manage.

"No. I cannot change my clothes in here, my lord. It is inappropriate."

He raised a perfectly arched eyebrow at her and for the first time, she noticed that he had that aristocratic, no-nonsense glare absolutely perfected. She felt like a small girl in the schoolroom again.

"No? You want to arrive at the next inn looking like a bedraggled stray cat, do you, Lady Emily?"

"I do not look like a stray cat."

He lifted a clump of her hair which had fallen out of her simple but stylish coiffure and lifted it to her gaze. It was muddy and wet, as he lifted it to her nose, she smelled wet hair. She glanced down at her gown which was absolutely covered in mud and clung to her in all the wrong places. She probably did resemble a stray cat. A bedraggled one at that. He reached across the seat and started to pull things out of his valise. Clean breeches, a clean shirt, stockings, waistcoat, a long neckcloth, and a spare coat.

"What do you need out? A gown, underskirts, a shift, stays, and stockings?" She did not answer. She was not changing in front of him no matter what state she was in. He shrugged and started to pull things out of her valise too. Oh, he was a brute. When he pulled out her stays and shift she gave a little yelp of dismay and then covered her mouth. He leaned over to her and his breath warmed her ear. "I have seen a lady's undergarments before, Lady Emily. I have removed them and I am no stranger to them. Yours shall be no different."

She scrunched up her nose and turned her head away from him. "Do you think to make me feel better by parading the fact you have... had intimate relations with a multitude of other women before me, my lord? I assure you, it gives me no comfort."

He sighed heavily and rested his forehead on her shoulder. "Forgive me. I was trying to put you at your ease by making light of the fact you are not the first lady I will have seen without clothes on. It was crass and unkind to mention it."

"They were no ladies," she replied venomously.

"Some of them were widows, my dear. Would that I die before you, I would not wish you to spend your entire life in mourning for me. You should live your life to the full and if that means finding pleasure with some handsome young buck's bed and showing him how to please a woman, then for your own sake and that of our children's do it discreetly, but enjoy yourself and do not feel guilty. Do not let the jealousy of young ladies who have not yet experienced the pleasure of the marriage bed deter you. For one day soon, they shall know it."

"I do not believe you are speaking in hypotheticals, my lord."

"I hope my death is a hypothetical, my love. As I hope is yours. However, if you stay in wet clothes it may not be. I do not want you catching a chill. So, stop sulking and let me help you undress."

She heaved in a frustrated breath. He did have a point about her catching a chill, and she did not want to arrive at the next inn looking like a stray cat. She could feel his warm breath on her neck and it was terribly distracting. It was almost as if its warmth was melting her inner resolve the way one's breath melted an ice at Gunther's.

"Oh, very well," she conceded.

"Good, for I have undone quite a few of these buttons at the back of your gown while I was awaiting your answer and it would have been damned inconvenient to have to re-button them."

"You, my lord, are very presumptuous."

"I am. You're sensible when all is said and done, Emily, and you know the dangers of a chill. Now, the plan of action is to both get the dirty clothes off, rub the dirt off with the blankets, then wrap the dirty clothes in the blankets and don the clean clothes. We will hand the dirty clothes to the staff at the inn to clean them and give them a good tip for their services."

"Fine."

"I will undress first. It is better for me to be cold for longer. I can stand it for a longer time. The quicker you are changed and dry, the better. Can you help me with my jacket?" He turned and she helped him peel the wet wool from his broad shoulders. His shirt was only a little soggy underneath but she knew it was wetter at the front. Taking off his boots took some minutes as they were so well fitting and there really was very little room in the carriage. He removed his stockings and garters, then his waistcoat and shirt. He was wet on the front of his chest and on his legs.

Then he undid the buttons of his breeches, lifted his bottom and slid them off over strong, muscular thighs, but it wasn't that which had her attention caught and held. It was the long thick member which jutted out from between his legs.

Emily licked her lips which suddenly seemed very dry. Feeling it through his breeches or against her leg the other night was a whole different thing to seeing it. He was drying himself on the blanket, rubbing his back, lifting his bottom to dry it and the backs of his thighs. Then he pulled it from under him, rubbed his chest and flat stomach, he gave a cursory swipe between his legs then dried his thighs and calves.

It was only then Gideon looked at her and his gaze followed hers.

"I apologise. For some reason, arguing with you arouses me. The thought of seeing you naked also arouses me. I am a mere man. I cannot do anything to hide the fact that I am aroused. If you ignore it, so can I. Turn around and I can finish your buttons."

Emily did as she was told. Why did she feel so excited at seeing it?

"Gideon?"

"Hmm."

"It still looks far too large."

He chuckled. "You do a man's ego a lot of good, Emily, but you, my dear, are such a curious young thing that you will be teaching me tricks soon. I am surprised that you have not already learned to pleasure yourself."

"Pleasure myself?"

"Yes. I would have thought you would have explored your own body. For someone so desperate to find out everything, you have a serious lack of curiosity about yourself."

"Oh, you mean touching myself between my legs?"

"Yes."

"Mother told me never to do that. When I was about twelve she sat me down and explained courses to me and told me how to deal with the bleeding and said apart from washing myself, I should never touch myself there."

"Did she? Yet you let me touch you." She was pushing her gown off her shoulders.

"You will be my husband. She did not say anything about husbands."

He took his own blanket and rubbed her hair. It was nice to know that he was taking care of her and despite her slight discomfiture that they would both be naked in this carriage for a few moments, she would soon be in clean dry clothes.

"Lift your arm so I can loosen your stays." She did as she was told and drew in a deep breath as the restrictive garment was released. He undid it at the back and removed it tossing it onto his pile of clothing. "Undo the ribbon of your shift."

She did and he eased it off her shoulders and arms to pool along with her gown at her waist. She felt so exposed, but he was sitting there naked too. Gideon took the blanket, rubbed gently on her back, shoulders and down her arms. She sat meekly like a child whose nurse was drying her after a bath.

When he wrapped his arm around her and began to dry her stomach and under her breasts, she made no protest. She knew she should. The rough woollen material was grazed gently over her nipples and upper chest. Her body seemed to be on fire at the touch of the cloth but she knew it was not because the material was rougher than a linen she would usually use.

She tried to undo the bow at her underskirts but her fingers were trembling.

"I cannot manage,"

"Let me." His voice was rough, as though he was getting a chill. She glanced around at his face. He was scowling hard. Was he disappointed in what she looked like without clothes? She lifted her breasts and glared at them. "Lift your bottom and I'll get the rest of your clothes off," he ground out, but she didn't move. She heard him but she was too worried about her breasts. Really, they were horrible. "Emily. For God's sake, what's wrong now?"

"It's my nipples. They're too big."

"What the devil?"

"I knew they were not right when my breasts started to grow but I had no one to ask and now.... now?"

He pulled her against him and pressed a couple of fingers over her mouth.

"Emily, your breasts, what I can see of them, are lovely. If we were not on a highway heading towards an inn at this precise moment, I would have you on my knee and I would be sucking each of them into my mouth in turn and feasting on them. You would be in seventh heaven. I am currently hanging on to my sanity by a thread. You are the most infuriating, yet most innocently sensual woman I have ever met. Without realising it, you have given me an almost constant cock-stand since I met you. Now, lift that delicious little arse of yours so I can get you naked and re-clothed before I do something we shall both regret."

Emily did not know what to make of his little diatribe, and what was a cock-stand. She had heard Robert calling his manhood a cock when he was growing up. He had done it to shock her a time or two. She was not going to ask Gideon though. Not when he was in this mood, but he had said he liked her breasts. Well, he said he wanted to suck on them. That must be good. The idea of him doing that sent a shiver of pleasure through her and he tugged impatiently on her clothing.

She lifted her bottom and he pushed all her clothing apart from her stockings to a heap on the floor. Then he swept around her skin with a blanket, rubbing with more vigour than she felt was necessary.

Just then the carriage hit a particularly large rut on the road. Emily had been using Gideon's thigh and the arm of the seat to lift herself. It had been a precarious position. Now she was flung across his lap.

She was just scrambling off his lap when they hit another rut. Emily reached for something to give her purchase and get her back to her own seat. An arm... but that was no arm. That was definitely *not* an arm.

Gideon groaned and his hand closed over hers. Instead of unfurling her fingers as she thought he would, he started to move their hands up and down his hard shaft.

Emily managed to right herself and looked up into Gideon's eyes, He looked conflicted.

"Better to go to hell, then to Bedlam, wouldn't you agree, my lady?"

"I think you may prefer seventh heaven, my lord."

He chuckled. Then he looked sombrely at her. "Do you wish to stop?"

She shook her head. "I like the feel of it in my hand. It's soft and yet hard at the same time."

"Come and sit on my lap then and I shall give you pleasure too. Bring your blanket." She did as she was bid and he grinned at her. She sat gingerly on his knee. "Tell me, which hand do you write with." She lifted her right hand. He took it and placed it on his long, thick staff, throwing his head back on an almost pained groan when she started to stroke him. He pressed his lips to hers as his fingers stroked through the curls at the apex of her thighs. She opened her legs without having to be told and his fingers slid through the slick folds easily. He stroked her deftly and she moved her hand to the same rhythm. The kiss was desperate and needy, he dragged his lips away kissing down her neck as he shifted her into his arms.

He brushed his lips over her chest and down onto her breast until he captured her nipple in his mouth. He held it between his teeth and worried it with his teeth.

"Gideon," she moaned, bucking against his fingers and gripping his shaft tighter.

"Yes, darling, that's it," he said before sucking her other nipple into his mouth and doing the same. "Damn, I'm not going to hold off."

"Gideon, it feels so good." Oh, she felt like a ninny saying that. He smiled indulgently down at her as he lifted his fingers to his mouth and licked them, taking some saliva from his tongue to spread on her folds. It was warm and added to the lovely wetness she already had,

"Imagine we are in my bed at Beattie Park, a bottle of wine and some chocolates next to the bed, my darling. My hard, thick, cock, sliding where my fingers are working, ready to make you mine. My lips trailing from your lips down your neck, down your body, stopping to pay homage to each of these delightful breasts, over your stomach, a little lick into your navel, and then down. My tongue trailing down, down, down, until it circles just here. "

Emily arched her back as her release pulsed through her. Little bright lights flashed under her eyelids and she was sure she might be having a fit of the vapours. That was unconscionable. Oh, how debasing. Her breathing was coming in heaving rasps and Gideon had pulled her against his chest. He was rubbing her back calling her a good girl.

She struggled out of his tight embrace and wiped her hair from her eyes. He was grinning.

"What is it?" she asked.

"You release like a firework at Vauxhall. It is a sight to behold. Now much though I would love to be a gentleman and pretend I do not need a release, you have been stroking me and I am afraid that even gentlemen only have so much tolerance for naked ladies and their very skilled manipulations. Shall I do it myself?"

"No, please, let me."

She curled her fingers back around his length and he leaned back against the squabs, closing his eyes and biting his bottom lip. He looked quite adorable. Soon, he was thrusting into her hand in time to her strokes. He put an arm around her to keep her safe. She slipped off his knee and sat beside him, allowing him more room to thrust. It seemed he wanted to but was afraid to harm her. He pulled her to his side and pressed a kiss to her temple.

She did not know where the urge came from but he had kissed her nipples. Suddenly she had stuck out her tongue and was circling the small dark nipple on his chest. He groaned, but it was a groan of pleasure.

"You like that?" she asked. He clasped his hand around hers and sped up the rhythm.

"Very much. Next, you'll be putting my cock in your mouth."

She raised her eyebrows.

"You want me to?" His eyes were closed.

"Yes," he ground out. "No," he shouted just as she tried to work out the best way to do it. "No, I... Christ..."

She was not sure there was any blood left in her fingers. His grip was so tight and they were stroking him so fast. He started to make a low moaning noise and then he tensed.

"Oh God!"

Jets of white liquid shot from the tip of it and landed on his chest. Some even landed on his chin and he wiped it away in what looked like annoyance. He stroked a few more times as a little more of the seed was squeezed from the tip and then Gideon let go. He uncurled her fingers from his purple headed shaft and raised it to his lips.

"Thank you," he said through his pants. "Thank you and I apologise."

"What are you apologising for?"

"A lady should not see a gentleman do that."

"I thought this lady had done it to the gentleman with a little help, of course."

Without lifting his head from the squabs, he turned it to her and smiled. It was a genuine, warm smile.

She looked at the white liquid adorning his chest.

"Is it sticky?"

"Not much, no."

"Can I touch it?"

"Over the years, my lady I hope to put plenty of it inside you but if Lady Curious wants to touch it and satisfy her curiosity before her wedding day, then she can."

She ran her finger through it. It was simply wet. How terribly uninteresting. As she raised it to her nose, he raised an eyebrow. It smelled, well, of nothing. She stuck out her tongue and watched his reaction. He did not try to stop her. She sucked her finger into her mouth.

"I wonder if hell has its own Bedlam," he mused.

"It tastes of salt...and something else."

"Well, it is the seed that babies come from."

Oh, she hadn't thought of that. Suddenly she was horrified. His eyes crinkled at the corners as he threw his head back and laughed. "You shall not end up with child by putting it in your mouth."

She pursed her lips. He was laughing at her. How was she supposed to have known that? Would he laugh at her and tell his friends she'd thought she could get pregnant by sucking his seed into her mouth. Would she be the talk of White's?

"We should get dressed."

"We should, but why are you upset with me?"

"I am not upset with you."

"Emily!"

"Promise me you shall not tell anyone I did not know I could not get pregnant by putting your seed in my mouth."

"Of course, I shall not."

"Promise me."

"Fine. I promise. Why do you need a promise?"

"I do not wish to be the talk of White's, or to be ridiculed."

"Firstly, my club is Brooks' and secondly, why would I discuss what happens in my own bedchamber, or in this case, my own carriage, with people I meet in Brooks'?"

"Robert was always telling his friends about the silly things I said or did."

"It sounds like your brother is an ass."

"He can be."

"What happens between us, is strictly between us. Just as you may not want anyone to know you didn't know everything there was to know about the making of babies before you were wed. I believe I would prefer it not to be known that I had an innocent young lady stroking me to completion in a carriage halfway to Scotland while we were both naked. While I have thoroughly enjoyed this interlude, Emily, I doubt I come out of it looking like much of a gentleman."

She giggled and passed him her blanket to wipe his chest.

"I did enjoy it too, if that is any consolation."

"It is all the consolation I need."

"We should get dressed. We must be getting near to that inn."

"Indeed."

Chapter 15

He was inordinately fond of her, it seemed. That was the conclusion that Gideon came to as he sat in the bath looking at his bride to be as she lay on the bed a few hours later.

They had arrived at the inn only to find that there was only one room left. Emily looked a little pale and he suspected the shock she had received from nearly being killed by that carriage was contributing to her state. He really had no wish to carry on. Also, it was Sunday. Maybe this was what came of travelling on the Sabbath. It was the reason the inn was full so early in the day. Few people had travelled that day. Only him, the godless creature that he was, and he had debauched Lady Emily in his carriage.

He really did deserve to go to hell.

It had been wonderful though and it was not as if he was not going to marry the chit. Of course, he was. He had wanted to push his fingers inside her this afternoon but had refrained. She should be untouched in there on her wedding night. Even though he had to share a bed with her tonight, he would not touch her and he would not sully her further.

Though sully was probably the wrong word. She had enjoyed it and she had been more than willing. She'd understood what she had been doing and he'd given her the opportunity to leave his cock alone and get dressed. She had liked the feel of him. He smiled at that.

A rustling from the bed caught his attention and he looked up to see her propped on her elbows. He had stayed in the tap room while maids had bathed her and readied her for bed. He had organised dinner for later to be brought to their room and hot bricks to warm her in bed.

"Are you well?" he enquired.

She wiped her face with her hand and scowled. "Why have you put me to bed like a naughty child?"

"I had the maids put you to bed to warm you up. You looked like a ghost when we arrived here. I wanted to care for you, not punish you. You've had a terrible shock. You were nearly killed."

"You had a terrible shock too."

"True but men are made of sterner stuff and I was not the one nearly killed. Now lie back down so I can get out of this bath without you gawping at me."

"I have seen you naked before."

"Y-e-s, and look how that ended."

Her blue eyes twinkled and he laid his head back against the tub. "I quite enjoyed how it ended actually."

"Yes, well there shall be no repeat of it until we are married. I have to face your brother and I want to be able to tell him I have not debauched you. Well, at least not fully."

"Oh, well, that is a little disappointing, I must admit. I thought since we were sharing a bed..."

"No, Emily. You shall be a virgin on your wedding night. I shall keep my hands to myself from now on."

"It was not your hands I was thinking of, Gideon."

Was she making a joke about his cock? Good God, she was. She was going to be the death of him. Dashed little hoyden that she was, but she made him smile and laugh, and God knew that given the current state of the country with this terrible weather and the failing crops, there was dashed little to laugh about.

"I shall be keeping *that* far away from you until our wedding night too. No more grabbing onto it as an excuse because there are ruts in the road, Lady Emily."

"But what if there is nothing else to hold on to, my lord? You would not want me to be injured."

"I swear, my lady, if you touch it again before our wedding night, I shall tie you up in my carriage and recite Homer to you for the rest of the journey—in Greek."

"The Iliad or the Odyssey?" she asked. Impertinent little wench.

"Both," he roared as he rose out of the bath, not caring that she was seeing him in all his naked glory yet again. Damn, this woman, she was frustrating, irritating, and damned wonderful. He just needed to be allowed to bed her, but his conscience would not allow him to go that far.

She lay there and watched him as though she was in a box at the theatre watching a play. She didn't avert her eyes, or blush, or feign modesty. He concentrated on drying himself. His upper body, his wet hair and then his lower body. He was half-erect from her scrutiny. He was getting aroused by the fact that she was not the shrinking violet an innocent lady should be. He kept imagining striding over to the bed, pulling back the covers, insinuating himself between her legs and taking her. Quickly he pulled on a pair of clean breeches and a shirt. He would put on his stockings, neckcloth and waistcoat later. Dinner would not be served for another couple of hours and he did not much care if the men who came up for the tub saw him in a state of undress. He would pull the curtains around the bed so they would not see Emily in her nightgown.

She was still watching him and he could not help but be drawn to her. He crawled onto the bed and pulled her into his arms, him on top of the covers and her below.

"You should try to sleep for at least an hour."

"I am not at all sleepy."

"You were too busy peeping at me in my bath, were you not? It seems mighty unfair, Lady Emily, when I was in the taproom while you bathed."

"So, you would like to see me naked again."

"What one wants and what one should have are two different things. I would like a kiss, however." He leaned over her and waited. She lifted her hand and drew his head down.

Gideon could not have said how long he kissed Emily for. It was a long time. He had never kissed anyone for so long or so thoroughly or with such gentle passion, but he enjoyed every minute. Normally a kiss was simply a prelude to sex. He never kissed innocents at balls. That was what one did if they were looking for a leg-shackle and until now, he had avoided that like the plague.

When there was a rap on the door, he called out to the men outside to wait for a minute. He drew the curtains around the bed and then let the men in. As they dragged the hip bath out, he smiled to himself at the memory of her lying in the bed, her lips swollen, her chin red from his day beard and a faint blush colouring her cheeks when he winked at her just before he pulled the drapes tight. Was Lady Emily developing a tendre for him? Was she fascinated by more than just the size of what was inside his breeches?

When the door clicked shut he opened the curtains. Emily was looking dismayed.

"What's wrong now?" he asked, sounding harsher than he meant.

"Do you think they thought we were... well... you know?"

"Emily, considering you are an innocent, your mind seems to constantly be straying to the topic of sex. I told the staff, you had fallen, hence the dirty clothes. They no doubt thought you were sleeping, which is what you are supposed to be doing."

"I do not feel like sleeping."

He walked over to his valise, opened it and pulled out a book. He deposited it on the bed beside her. "Then read. Though I am not sure you should be reading books with romantic themes like Mansfield Park. You have a vivid enough imagination as it is."

"Perhaps I should become an author."

"Heaven forbids. I hate to think what lurid gothic novel would come out of that unfettered imagination of yours."

She picked up the book and started to flick through it. She was not reading. She was not even trying to find her page, for he had given her a bookmark and it was sticking out of the book. She was frowning. Her head was down. Was she upset?

Suddenly she tossed the book aside and turned onto her side, curled up into a ball.

"Emily?"

"I am tired. I should sleep."

"You are upset with me. I was teasing."

"No, Gideon. You were not. What you say is true, even if you were."

He sighed. This was not silly female hysterics. The young lady he was about to marry was crippled by self-loathing and self-doubt. Even some gentle teasing made her feel worthless and while someone else would laugh it off, Emily took it to heart. In many ways, he was glad he'd had this time alone with her before they wed. Now he knew. Now he could help her. He wasn't sure how but he could do something.

"Emily?" She sniffed. It told him that she was crying but also that she had heard him. "Emily, my darling, please sit up and listen to me." He had no clue what he was going to say, but whatever it was, it was going to come from the heart.

"I think you should not marry me, my lord. Leave me at my brother's house. I shall be fine. I do not need to go back to town. You shall not be harmed by the scandal of a failed elopement. I can stay in the country and tend the garden."

"Not in this weather. Who knows how many years this rain might go on for."

She turned onto her back and wiped her wet eyes. "That is not funny, my lord. People are beginning to starve. You said so yourself."

"I know, but it's not funny that you think yourself so unworthy of marriage, a home and happiness that you would throw it over because I was teasing you."

"But what you say is true, my lord. I speak out of turn, I am clumsy, I nearly got myself killed today, I do not think before I act, I let my imagination run away with me, I have been wholly inappropriate. I am obsessed with the act of... sex." Her eyes were wide with horror. He wanted to laugh but he tamped down the urge. He placed his hands under her shoulders and pulled her into his embrace. She resisted at first and then her arms were around him and fresh tears were flowing. He allowed her to weep. He had a feeling this was years of pain she was letting go.

He pressed kisses into her hair as her sobs subsided and she started simply to sniffle. He had no handkerchief on him. Stroking his hand down her long braid, he spoke.

"You have told me what you think of yourself and how you believe others view you, now let me have my say. I may not have known you more than a week or so, but I am coming to know a delightful, funny, intelligent, witty, sensual, beautiful young woman who is curious about the world around her. We are both very different kinds of people, Emily. We need to learn to live together and learn each other's ways. That's the case in all marriages, I would presume. You have given me a litany of what you perceive to be your faults. I could give you a long list of my faults. It seems to me that you only see your faults and none of the wonderful things that everyone else sees. Take Sophia for instance."

"What about Sophia?"

"Do you trust her?"

"Of course. She is my very dear friend."

"And you are hers. She trusts you, she likes you—nay loves you, as she speaks of you often. Do you think my sister a ninny?"

"Indeed not."

"Then why do you doubt her judgement when it comes to choosing friends? She chose you. She likes you. Sophia sees many wonderful gifts that you have."

Emily pulled back and gave him a sceptical look. "I feel like you have tricked me by using your sister."

"There is no trick. Sophia makes up her own mind about people and, as you know, she does not suffer fools gladly."

"That is true." Emily smiled. He had a feeling she was remembering something that Sophia had said or done about some young lady of the Beau-Monde.

"Let me find you a handkerchief. I have no doubt that we have quite a distance to go before you feel happy about who you are and what type of person you are, Lady Emily, but I shall be your husband and I shall be there with you every step of the way."

"Even when I fall flat on my face?"

"With luck, I shall be there to catch you every time."

Chapter 16

Three evenings later, Gideon's carriage trundled up the private road onto the Aelton Manor estate—the principal seat of the Earl of Whitsnow.

Gideon placed his gloved hand over hers. They had put on their hat, bonnet, gloves and were sitting up straight and ready to meet the Earl. Emily just hoped he was home... or did she? Perhaps it would be better if he was away to London.

The weather seemed better up here and the ground not so sodden. Perhaps there was not so much work to be done and Robert could be enjoying what little was left of the Season.

There were candles lit in the drawing room, she could see. There was definitely someone in residence. She sighed heavily.

"Come now. The worst that will happen is he will kill me."

Emily glared at Gideon.

"That is not funny, my lord."

He lifted her gloved hand to his lips and kissed it as the carriage slowed. "Worst thing that can happen. Most likely he will force us to marry."

A footman opened the door and let down the steps. Gideon got out and handed Emily down.

"Welcome home, my lady."

The footman bowed.

"Good evening Wilson. How is your Mama?"

"Very well, my lady," said the footman, giving a sidelong look at Gideon.

"Very pleased to hear it. I shall be in my own room tonight and Lord Beattie will be in the blue room."

"The Green room is made up for Lord Beattie, my lady."

"Oh? That is too far away. The Blue room is fine."

"But his lordship..."

"His lordship said the green room." Emily looked up to see the bellowing figure in the doorway beside a slightly flustered looking Mr Lang, the butler. Emily had never seen Mr Lang look flustered in her life.

"Robert, darling."

"Emily, go to your room." She glanced down and saw a pistol in her brother's hand.

"No," she said once she had arrived at her brother's side. "This is between you and me. You shall not harm Lord Beattie. It is my fault he had to elope with me. This is my doing."

"Of course, it is, Emily. You are an imbecile."

"How dare you Whitsnow. That is my affianced bride whom you insult." Emily rolled her eyes. She could almost hear her mother as she shook her head *Boys will be boys.*

"She is my sister. She may be a ninny but how dare you debauch her."

"He has not debauched me. I am an innocent. Now can we take this inside before you let all the servants know our business?"

Robert glared at Gideon.

"He has not touched you?"

Emily drew in her breath. "He has been the perfect gentleman." She had not exactly lied but she had not exactly answered his question. She hoped he would not notice.

"Fine. Come up to the drawing room." He passed his pistol to the butler. "Please ask Staines to put that back in the box in my study."

"Aye, my lord." Robert then pulled Emily into a hug. "I was worried about you," he confided. "Aunt Gertrude's letter said you had been spirited away to Scotland and she was not sure if Beattie's intentions were honourable."

He let her go. "Of course, they are."

She and Gideon had said the same words at the same time. She laughed.

"I left your aunt a letter explaining what was going on," Gideon said. "I thought I had given her sufficient explanation to set her mind at ease. Apparently not."

"Aunt Gertrude always was a worry wart."

They were climbing the stairs to the drawing room. When they got to the top, two footmen opened the large double doors to allow them to walk in.

"Did you order a tea tray to be brought up?"

"No need, we shall be dressing for dinner soon. Dinner is in an hour. I presume you did not eat."

"No. Not yet."

"Good."

He motioned for them to sit. She did not like having to sit so far apart from Gideon after a week of being cramped beside him in a carriage, but, appearances must be upheld.

"So, you are to marry my sister, Beattie, eh?"

"With your permission. of course."

"You do not need his permission in Scotland," Emily started but Gideon gave her a look that told her to hold her tongue. She shut her mouth.

"As your sister rightly says, I do not necessarily need your permission, but I would prefer it. I'd rather not have to leave here with us both cowering from your pistol fire, but marry her, I shall."

Robert waved his hand as if almost bored. "You may as well. Better that than she ends up on the shelf and living in the dower house for eternity." Then he turned to Emily. "He's sleeping in the green room and you shall be in there with him tomorrow night. It is suitably far enough away from my apartments that I won't hear your screams when he breaks your maidenhead."

Emily's eyes widened and she turned to look at Gideon, who rolled his eyes and gave her an almost imperceptible shake of his head. His eyes—those green eyes—told her to trust him and she did. Her brother was being a pig, as he always was.

"My dear man, if you make your women scream, then you're not doing it properly," said Gideon, affecting the same fashionable ennui as was Robert. It was almost comical from Gideon.

"You speak like this in front of ladies, Beattie."

"You were the one to bring up maidenheads, my dear chap. I thought perhaps you spoke like this in front of your sister all the time. Personally, I would never have considered speaking like this in front of dear lady Emily in such a vulgar manner had you not begun the conversation. My dear Lady Emily, how can you ever forgive me?"

Emily wanted to laugh. She schooled her features into her most understanding expression and nodded.

"Lord Beattie, I accept your apology. I believe my brother is just trying to make me frightened, as he did on the night of my come-out ball and the afternoon I made my curtsey to the Queen. He told me such terrible stories of all the tragedies that might occur. Only two bad things happened. I ripped the hem of my dress on the way home from my curtsey when I tripped over my dress. Luckily, Robert managed to catch my arm and stop me from ending face first on the ground, and I spilt a little champagne on my dress at the ball, because of all the decoration. However, no one noticed."

"Such a clumsy girl, Emily," Robert said, rolling his own eyes.

She sighed and got to her feet. "Well, if you are finished trying to make me look like an idiot in front of my fiancé I shall show him to the green bedchamber."

"I think not. You are not to be trusted alone together."

"Oh Robert, we have been alone for a week together with just a coachman and a stable hand. If he has not debauched me yet, I doubt Lord Beattie shall debauch me before dinner."

"Well no, I do like to be thorough." Gideon was grinning down at her, one eyebrow raised. Heat flooded her cheeks. She glanced at Robert who was looking at them both through narrowed eyes. Did he suspect, as was true, that slightly more had gone on during the trip than they had confessed?

That said, the past few days, Gideon had been a perfect gentleman, much to her chagrin. They had not been forced to share a bed again, and on Sunday night when they'd had to share, Gideon had rolled away from her after kissing her slowly and softly good night.

When they arrived at his room, he raised her hand to his lips and pressed a kiss to the back of it.

"It may hurt a little, Emily, but I promise to be as gentle as I can."

"I know you will. I trust you."

She turned and started to walk away.

"Emily!" She turned at his voice. "You are beautiful and delightful."

Emily smiled. "Thank you." As she turned to walk away she tripped, over her own silly feet.

She righted herself immediately and circled her ankle. She had probably swivelled around too quickly on her heel again. Stupid girl. She considered her ankle but she was sure it was fine. And then large arms were around her waist.

"Did you hurt yourself."

Emily giggled. "No, silly. I am fine. Let me go before someone sees."

"Is this what always happens?"

"I do not understand?"

"When you say you are clumsy?"

"Oh, all manner of things. I bump into things, I knock things over, I trip, I stumble. It has happened all my life. The doctor can find nothing wrong with me. I had no difficulties with my lessons. I was not very good at catching balls and playing the piano. That is why I sing. I am musical, I just could never make my left hand and right-hand work together. Now Gideon, I must get ready for dinner. I am unharmed as you can see."

He sighed but pressed the lightest kiss to her neck.

"Be careful."

"I shall."

Chapter 17

The next morning was sunny. Emily could not believe her eyes. It was actually a sunny day. It had been months since she had seen the sun and it was shining on her wedding day. She had spoken to the maid the evening before about what she should wear. A dress which had been hanging up in her wardrobe was just the thing. It was yellow and had lace trim. It was not too fancy but not too drab.

Beryl, the maid, had suggested wearing it with her pearls and a bonnet decorated with roses. She had assured Emily that there were roses growing in the gardens of Aelton Manor. She had organised the head gardener to pick enough roses for her bonnet, a small bouquet for her and to pin on the jackets of the Viscount and the Earl, assuming the Earl would accompany them over the border.

She hoped he would but there was no guarantee.

She had breakfasted in her room, rather than going down to meet the men. They would be leaving early for the border.

She was standing in the large foyer, at the bottom of the sweeping staircase, feeling a little lost, when Robert strode out of his study and stopped. She noticed he had a rosebud pinned to his jacket. Did this mean he was accompanying them?

"Good God, Em, look at you."

"Oh! I did not think to bring anything, well... I..."

"You look like a proper lady. Mama and Papa would be so proud of you." He was scowling as he said it but his eyes looked suddenly very bright.

"Oh Robert, you are a beast."

"In what way am I a beast? I am complimenting you."

"You shall make me cry on my wedding day."

He walked over to her and enveloped her in a great big embrace. "I've only ever wanted you to be happy, Tiny."

"You have not called me Tiny since I was about five years old. You always called me clumsy, or Ninny."

"Yes, well I sat and drank rather a lot of port with your fiancé last night. I was planning to give him a piece of my mind. It turned out, he gave me a piece of his mind. He told me that you have a rather low opinion of yourself because you think these things about yourself."

She pulled away from him and swiped at her wet eyes. "It is true though."

"Perhaps, but it seems to be something you cannot control or you would. I am a prize ass for being a beast about it. Beattie is quite right. I have not helped matters. More than likely it just makes you more nervous and more likely to get yourself into bother."

"He said that."

"He seems to care very deeply for you."

"I sort of forced his hand. I did not mean to. I was a ninny."

"He explained what happened. "

"You are not angry with him?"

Robert sighed and wiped a hand across his face. "I wish he had waited and married you by special licence instead of eloping. It's still a bit of a scandal, in all honesty, Em. I understand why he did it. We might live far from town up here but you know we do still get the papers, albeit a few days late. I know what is happening in the south of the country and on the continent. We have not worked out the particulars. We shall discuss it on the way to Scotland. I shall bring my horse with us tied to the coach so that I can travel home more quickly. I have work to do."

"I understand. Thank you for coming with us."

"I would never refuse to attend my own sister's wedding, Em. Come, I think we have left your fiancé waiting in the coach long enough. I think that is punishment enough."

"You left him in the coach? Robert!"

Robert chuckled. "I may be willing to let up on being a beast to you, Tiny, but your fiancé has years left to catch up."

She punched him on the arm, refused to take his sleeve and marched out of the house on the way to her wedding.

∞ ∞ ∞

"Well, Scottish weddings are not too bad."

They were sitting in a private parlour in an inn just back over the English border from Gretna Green after the wedding, and that was the considered opinion of the Earl of Whitsnow. Gideon swallowed his mouthful of wine and nodded his head.

"Not bad at all. It appears that we are properly and legally wed, my love." Gideon grinned at the new Lady Beattie, she blushed and smiled coyly at him over the rim of her own wine glass.

Was the little tease thinking about what he was thinking about? He had a damned hard cock, despite the presence of her brother. Luckily, he still had two more courses to get his traitorous body under control, and Whitsnow was not sharing their carriage back to Aelton Manor.

"Really Beattie. Are you intending to make cow eyes at my sister for the rest of the meal? If so, I may just get on my horse now and go home. This is supposed to be a celebratory meal, not the damned prelude to your consummation."

Gideon shook his head. "I do apologise, my good man. I was distracted for a moment. I have had a certain lack of sleep the last week. As you know, it is difficult to sleep when one is not in one's own bed, and I suspect I have not fully recovered from the injury I sustained to my head."

"Y-e-e-s, possibly," Whitsnow had raised an eyebrow and did not look convinced. Gideon gave him his most innocent expression but had the most horrible feeling he was failing miserably.

Eventually, their meal was over. Emily had been correct. Her brother did live very close to the Scottish border. Robert jumped onto his horse, waved to them and dashed off. Gideon handed his wife—he liked the sound of that—up into the carriage and followed her in.

He sat down beside her, placed his arm around her shoulder and pulled her to his side.

As soon as they were out of the inn yard and trundling along the highway, Gideon untied her bonnet and tossed it onto the seat opposite. He then removed his own hat and discarded it likewise.

Then he lifted her bodily onto his lap.

"Husband?"

"Lady Beattie, you make me very hard when you call me that."

She feigned innocence.

"Really Lord Beattie. Which part of you, in particular, gets hard?"

He peppered little kisses along her jawline and she sighed. A truly feminine sigh that went straight to his groin.

"My cock, Lady Beattie. My cock gets hard. Call me *husband* again."

"My lord, are we going to make love in the carriage?"

He chuckled.

"No, my lady. We are not. You shall not be arriving back at your brother's house looking completely tumbled. You shall arrive looking like a lady."

"Then why, pray tell, am I on your lap, and why do you want me to make you hard?"

"You are on my knee because I am allowed to put you on my knee and no one can say a damned thing about it. I just wanted to hear you call me *husband.* I do not care that it makes me hard. I love when you do it."

She sighed and rested her forehead against his. "I like being on your lap, husband. You make me feel safe, and cherished."

"Then let us just enjoy being in one another's company, wife. Rest your head on my shoulder and we shall just enjoy being together for a while." He rested his own head back against the squabs and soon they were both dozing.

He woke when the carriage turned into the private road up to Aelton Manor. He shook his sleeping wife awake. She looked a little tousled but not tumbled. She had the imprint of his jacket on the skin of her face.

"I must look a complete fright."

"You look beautiful."

"What will Robert say."

"Robert can go to the devil."

"Yes, I suppose he can. I am your concern now."

"You are indeed."

Robert was holed up in his study when they arrived back and was not to be disturbed, according to the butler. They could go wherever they wished in the house and grounds. He had arranged for them to be sent dinner to their apartment at eight o'clock. If that did not suit, they were to inform the housekeeper.

Emily was looking a little askance at this information and looked up at him as if not sure how to proceed.

"It is a lovely day. We could go for a stroll around the park. I have missed the sunshine, I must confess."

"Oh, I have too. Yes, let us go for a walk."

Colour came back to her cheeks and she led the way back out the door. They walked in silence for a while through some well-tended gardens until they arrived at what appeared to be the beginning of a wilderness walk.

Gideon spoke up.

"Back at the house, you looked afraid as though I was going to jump on top of you and ravish you right there and then, but in the carriage, you seemed rather keen on the idea."

She pursed her lips and looked past him. She clearly did not wish to meet his gaze.

"We were in high spirits in the carriage. If you had taken me there and then, I would not have had time to get nervous. I must admit though, I am a little afraid."

"Of what?"

"The pain. Of not being good enough. Of being clumsy and awkward."

He nodded. He understood her concerns. He was sure had he stopped long enough to consider his own worries when he had been a virgin, he would have had the same concerns. However, he had followed the direction his cock was pointing in. He'd drunk a little too much of his father's brandy and tumbled his sister's very young governess. It had come as a shock to him that the very young governess was older than she'd looked and was, in fact, not a virgin. She'd taught him a thing or two, been a very skilled lover and instructed more than his sister that Season. Sadly, she had found herself a vicar to marry, obviously convinced him she was an innocent young lady and he never saw or heard from her again once she headed off to rural Shropshire.

"I have no concerns, my love. You are a quick learner. You were very adept at bringing me pleasure that day in the carriage when we had to change out of our muddy clothes. I understand the pain is fleeting as long as I only take you once and prepare you properly, which I shall."

She nodded in understanding.

"Am I being a ninny about this?"

"Anything we have not yet experienced is bound to give us a certain amount of apprehension, so no, you are not a ninny about this. You did say you trusted me. Trust me now that I can make the experience good for both of us."

She drew his face down and pressed a delicate kiss to his lips.

"Yes, you are correct. I do trust you. Thank you for being so understanding."

"Show me around the rest of this park and let us enjoy the sunshine before we must return to rainy old Herefordshire."

∞ ∞ ∞

Never mind going to hell, Gideon Beattie believed he may be beatified when he died if this week was anything to go by. He had just spent an hour watching Lady Emily Beattie eating her dinner, her tongue sticking out to lick her lips, her lips wet from the wine in her glass, her bosom almost spilling out of her evening dress and her cheeks almost scarlet every time he looked at her. He was changing in the dressing room off the green bedroom and could hear the murmurs of voices, Emily and her maid in the room next door.

He stroked his hard shaft in the hope of getting some sort of relief from the persistent ache.

At last, he heard the outer door of the room click shut. He waited a moment and knocked.

"Emily, may I come in?"

"Uh, yes, I suppose you may."

"Well, you know how to make your husband feel welcome," he said, the sarcasm evident in his tone as he walked into the room. Expecting to see her sitting at a window or her dressing table in a nightgown, waiting for him, he was surprised to see her naked, scrambling into the large four-poster bed.

"Where is your nightgown?" he asked.

"There." She pointed to the chair where a nightgown lay discarded.

"Why are you already naked?"

She frowned. "I understood that to be the point, Gideon. Oh, give me the nightgown." She started to scramble back out the bed but he hurried to her and caught her by the hips.

"No, you are right. That is the point. Do you ever have a moment thought out in your head so many times that when it does actually happen, it is not how you imagined it and you say entirely the wrong thing?"

She chuckled. "Frequently."

"All week I have imagined this moment, but you were sitting at the window in your nightgown and I came over and pulled you to your feet and kissed you on the lips then led you to the bed. Instead, my hands are already on your bare hips, my teeth.... tugging at your earlobe, your pert little bottom pressed against my erection. I must say, it does feel divine. Much better than in my imagination."

He moved his hand up and cupped her breast, brushing his hand over her erect nipple.

"Gideon!" Her voice was a breathy moan and his cock jerked against her bottom.

"Get on the bed and lie on your back while I remove this dressing gown."

She did as he asked and he was crawling between her knees and up her body seconds later.

She giggled nervously when his cock jerked and touched her stomach. He looked between them and smiled.

"He's happy to see you. He knows we are at last going to consummate this marriage."

"He?"

"It does sometimes feel as though it has a mind of its own, especially when I am near you." He moved to her side and onto his hip drawing her into a heated kiss. His tongue plundered her mouth as he moved his hand between her legs. She was tense—obviously worried about this moment. He had to get her to relax or it would be so much worse if her muscles were tight.

He moved his hand away from between her legs and just concentrated on kissing her again. When she threaded her fingers through his hair, moaning and rubbing her calf against his, he knew he was doing the right thing. She was responding as a lover should.

He broke the kiss and her lips trailed over his chin and down his neck. Damn, she was a sensual woman. She was clearly going completely on instinct, but it was his turn.

She was kissing his chest and trying to wriggle down the bed, her hand reaching for his shaft.

Devil take it. It was tempting to let her, but it would be all over in seconds and he would not disgrace himself on his wedding night, no matter how good it might feel in the moment. He caught her hand and brought it to his lips, kissing down the inside of her arm, warm, wet, sensual kisses, her skin was as soft as satin.

She was becoming pliant in his arms again instead of being the aggressor. Gideon would have no problem with Emily being in charge in the bedroom occasionally. He liked his woman to ride him to completion sometimes, but not tonight.

He kissed down her breast until he closed his mouth over the tip of one beautiful pink nipple. Yes, she did have large nipples and he loved them. Using the flat of his tongue to lick around the areola, the mewl of pleasure he pulled from her made him groan with need. He needed to be inside her soon.

He moved a hand between her legs. This time she opened for him easily. She was wet and wanting. As he stroked his fingers through her folds, she bucked into his touch.

He needed a plan. He would have sex with her, let her recover and then, since she would be sore, he could use his mouth on her later. She could use her hand. That would suffice. He already needed her again and he had not yet slaked his lust with her the first time.

He loved her breasts. She was so wet for him.

He pushed a finger inside her. She grabbed his shoulder.

"Gid..."

"Shh. I said I would prepare, you, my love." She relaxed onto the bed and he eased his finger in and out of her. Damn, she was so hot and tight. Her breasts were better than any dessert. He feasted on them. When she started to moan, he added a second finger. Her grip on his shoulder tightened slightly but then she sighed and allowed her knees to fall to the side. He flicked her pearl with his thumb.

"Oh, husband."

Christ, was she trying to send him over the edge?

"Do you like that wife?" His voice was deep and gravelly. He did not think he had ever been this aroused in his life. He had never had a virgin before, and though he had given her two releases on the way here, they had been fast and furious, he had felt a sense of unease both times. For though he had planned to marry her, he knew he had not yet done the deed. Now, however, she was his, she had his fingers buried in her as deep as they would go and she was on the edge of the precipice.

"Gideon, I..."

"Let go, my love," he urged.

"Gideon!" Her body went rigid and the gentle strokes she had been making through his hair became a painful pull. She arched off the bed and closed her eyes. He moved up the bed, the muscles inside her still pulsed around his fingers but he removed them and enveloped her in his embrace.

He held her as she wrapped her thighs around one of his and rubbed herself against him.

Then Gideon rolled her over. It was now or never.

"Bend your knees, my love."

She did as she was told and again she looked at him with hardly disguised terror. He placed a hand under her bottom and angled her slightly. Better to do it in one swift move once he was inside a small amount.

He pushed in. She did not scream in pain but her thighs were like bricks. He was only in past the head of his cock. He would never get past her maidenhead going this slowly.

He had noticed on the journey up that Emily was very easily distracted. She would start to tell a story, drift away for a second then tell a different story. He supposed she was unaware of this. But she was definitely very easy to misdirect.

"What is that?" He lifted her arm." She looked at the inside of her arm that he had just raised.

"What?"

Gideon leaned over her. He took the skin between thumb and forefinger and tweaked it.

"Ouch!" she yelled. He was aware of her body relaxing and he drove home.

"Sorry," he muttered. Damn, she felt good.

"Oh!" The look on the Viscountess Beattie's face was priceless.

Chapter 18

"You pinched me!" Emily exclaimed as Gideon covered her mouth with his and stopped the tirade she was about to unleash on him. Mmm, she did like his kisses. He stroked her tongue with his—long deliberate strokes which mimicked the long deliberate strokes of his...

Oh yes, that was really quite pleasant. There was a little discomfort, she supposed. Perhaps if she moved her legs around him. Would that be terribly gauche? Well, he had nipped her arm, so she did not care if she was gauche.

As she wrapped her legs around his hips, he moved her arms above her head and withdrew from the kiss. He smiled down at her, his gaze meeting hers, his eyes twinkling with suppressed mirth.

"You did that on purpose," Emily accused.

"Of course, I did. Are you in pain?"

"No." He pressed his lips to the point on her arm where he had nipped. Then he peppered kisses along her jaw and her neck. Emily could feel the now familiar tension building.

"Gideon, please."

Gideon seemed to search her gaze for a moment. Then he let go of her hands and gathered her to him, his hands underneath her. He started to move in and out of her with such speed that Emily could only cling to him, but it felt so good. Her body was afire with sensations, dripping with perspiration and her husband, his rough chin on her shoulder, his soft lips at her neck became almost mad with his need, driving himself in and out of her body.

Then the inferno became an explosion. She cried out his name and clung to him as pleasure assaulted her body, ripping through her. Gideon seemed to lose his speed and rhythm.

He cursed and tensed and she felt the warmth of his release inside her. He thrust into her a few more times and then his movements slowed until he was barely moving. He was making little kissing motions with his lips against her neck.

Emily ran her hands up and down his damp back. He had expended a lot of energy, she supposed. She was tired herself and he had done a lot more work than her.

She allowed her legs to drop onto the mattress and it was then that he lifted his head.

"I apologise. I must be heavy."

"No. It is fine. I like feeling you on top of me."

"Hmm." He raised a sceptical eyebrow. Then he moved his hips, disconnecting them. She winced. That did hurt a little. "Oh God, I hurt you."

"No. At least I do not think so." She tightened her muscles down there and felt no pain. He gave her a little rub. It felt nice. She hadn't realised she had moaned out loud until she looked up into his grinning face.

He lay down beside her and pulled her into his arms. "I do apologise for pinching your arm but it was the only way I could think to make you relax. I recall once cutting my knee and the bandage had stuck to my skin with the dried blood. I was making a real production of getting the thing removed. The best thing to do was to distract me from the pain, so my nurse pinched me on the arm and it relaxed me enough to have the bandage removed. There was really very little bleeding from the sore knee and it really did not hurt so very much. I hoped that it might help you if I distracted you long enough to break your maidenhead."

He really was rather sweet.

"Thank you. I did not notice it very much at all, and I did enjoy what we did."

"So, you are not averse to us having a full and active sex life, Lady Beattie?"

"Not if it is like that—no."

"It shall be better. Once we get better acquainted. Now let me find a cloth and water and I shall clean you up."

He left the bed and walked to the dressing table. He poured water from the pitcher into the bowl and dampened a linen. Then he brought the wet linen and a dry linen to the bed. He opened her legs and, with the greatest care and gentleness, he cleaned her most intimate area. Then he pressed a kiss—right there. He gave his own manhood a quick wipe and put the cloths back.

"Is there much blood?" she asked.

"A little. Do you ride astride, perchance?"

"Here in the country, yes, but never in Town."

"Because you are less likely to fall?"

"Yes. Is that very bad?"

"I cannot say I care very much either way, but it may be why there is less blood than one might expect. Though I must say, I have never had sex with a virgin before so I cannot say for sure how much blood one should expect."

"I am, I mean, I was a virgin. You do believe me, do you not?"

He smiled and climbed back into bed, pulling the bedclothes over them and encouraging her to lay in his arms. She went willingly.

"Of course, I believe you. You do not have it in you to tell lies, my love. You would be overcome with guilt and blurt out the truth."

He was not wrong.

"Do we just go to sleep now?" she asked, unsure of what should happen now.

"It is not particularly late. I shall not take you again tonight as I would not want you to get sore, but there are other things we can do that are equally pleasurable."

She ran her hands across the parts of his body she could reach and hugged him tighter. She liked being in bed with him, naked. He did not seem to mind if she was gauche when they were alone. Was she being gauche?

Her hand ran over his bare bottom and she gave the firm skin a little squeeze just to see what his reaction would be. He groaned and rolled her onto her back.

"I see you have become quite confident, Lady Beattie. You think that just because you have lost your virginity you are now a skilled seductress?" He was teasing her of course as he took one of her nipples into his mouth.

"I would never presume, husband."

He bit her nipple causing a little pain and she sucked in a breath, but as soon as she noticed the pain, he was soothing with his tongue. "What was that for?"

"I told you what effect you calling me *husband* has on me."

"I thought you liked that effect. You did not complain when we were naked in the carriage and I brought you to release with my hand."

"Don't remind me, wife. A man only has so much control. Now it is your turn to be brought to release...again."

He kissed down her stomach and opened her legs wide. He looked at her intimate area like a starving man would look at a feast.

"Gideon, I thought you were teasing about that."

"I never tease about sex, wife."

Then his tongue was on her, lapping, sucking, swirling. Somewhere in the middle of it, Emily could not help thinking she was glad that Robert had put them in the green room. Not because she was screaming in pain, but because her pleading was getting louder. She was begging Gideon for a release. The blasted man kept taking her to almost the peak then soothing her down again then repeating until she was almost out of her mind. The fifth time, as he chuckled into her flesh, she grabbed hold of his hair.

"Gideon, for God's sake, I am going to die." He did not laugh this time. Instead, he renewed his efforts and this time as she reached the peak, he allowed her to fall over it into sweet release. As she shuddered through it, he crawled up the bed and held her in his arms, crooning and stroking her back. His long thick erection jerked between them, leaving a little wet mark on her belly. He was correct, it did seem to have a mind of its own.

Emily remembered their time in the carriage when they had been naked. She had asked him if he wanted her to put his cock in her mouth. He had said yes, then changed his mind, concerned for her maiden sensibilities no doubt, but she was his wife now. What would he say now?

It was her turn to roll him onto his back. She expected that he would protest or roll her back but he did not. She straddled him and he did nothing but raise an imperious eyebrow at her. She gave a nervous little laugh as she licked his small dark nipple. That was when he took hold of her braid, removed the ribbon and loosened her hair to fall down over her back and shoulders.

"Beautiful," he murmured as he ran his hand through a large tress. She kissed down his stomach. When Gideon drew in a breath and held it, Emily did wonder if she was doing the correct thing. Now he was the tense one. She peppered little kisses down his long hard shaft and Gideon just stared at her, his expression implacable. Was she doing it correctly?

She took it in her hand and lifted it.

"Does this hurt?" She did not want to bend it in the wrong way.

"No." His voice was barely a whisper. "What are you planning to do with it now, Emily?"

What indeed?

She gazed at the purple head, weeping clear liquid and bit her lip. She had started this and she had to complete her mission. She caught his gaze and saw trust there. *He* trusted *her*. How had that happened?

"If I am doing it wrong or I hurt you, please say."

A slight smile curved his lips.

"I shall. Have no fear."

"I just put my mouth over it?"

"If you wish, and move it up and down. Your hand too."

She did as he suggested. His guttural moan as her lips and tongue made contact went straight through her.

He placed his hands into her hair and guided her gently

"Emily, that is so good." She smiled around him and continued her ministrations, but it was hard work and she began to tire. Her mouth was aching. Her hand was beginning to hurt. How had he managed to do what he had done to her for so long?

"Emily, come up here and kiss me. I need your kisses."

She let his large member go with a pop and he smiled at her, urging her back to the top of the bed. As she lay along his side, he took himself in hand and started to stroke himself. She looked down in disappointment.

"Thank you. That was wonderful."

"You haven't released yet."

"I'm very close, but you are tiring. Besides, I want you here by my side when I release."

Emily was not convinced. She had failed him and she could feel the burning of tears behind her eyes. He drew her into a kiss and her hands started to roam over his taut body. He took her roaming hand and placed them on his balls.

"Be gentle but explore them," he said. His own hand was stroking fast and he was biting his lip. She sucked his nipple into her mouth again. "Christ, you're perfect, Em."

Then the warm liquid splashed on her arm and side and onto his body too. His hard body slowly, ever so slowly, started to relax.

He rolled against her and kissed her slowly and sensually before flopping back on the bed and declaring himself spent.

Chapter 19

"I cannot believe that Robert gave you two carriages filled with goods and that we have dressed scarecrows in finery and placed them in the carriages to look like people. It is almost inspired," said Emily, as they drew out of Aelton Manor estate the next morning.

"I had not really thought of the logistics of transporting the goods myself, I must say." Gideon was tired and crotchety but was grateful to Robert for his sage advice. Of course, it was a robbery waiting to happen, especially once they got farther south where food was becoming scarce. Robert had given them oats and maize and some potato seeds. They did not have a lot as the horses could not pull large amounts. Robert had, however, given them his main coach which was large and needed four horses to pull it plus one other. He had been very generous. He had a large stable full of horses, explaining to Gideon that he often sent horses on ahead so that he could travel to London in faster stages, pushing the horses to go farther in a day than Gideon himself had been happy to do.

Without any humans or baggage inside the two spare coaches, they were able to fit in quite a few sacks of grain. They would travel slowly back down to Herefordshire and give the horses plenty of time to recuperate each evening. Robert had promised to send more grain as soon as Gideon sent back the carriages.

"Given my brother was going to blow your brains out only two days ago, he has had a fine change of heart, has he not?"

Gideon sighed. "While I agree your brother is a prize ass and has treated you abominably, he is a peer of the realm and he was brought up to do his duty. In this case, it is to help out those in need, Emily."

"I know he's a good man. I never doubted it. I doubted myself. I still do."

"What is it that you doubt?"

"That I shall be a good wife and mother."

"My darling, I am sapped of energy this morning. Your brother kept giving me knowing looks over his newspaper. I have no complaints about your..." he waved an arm as he searched for the correct word. "...abilities as a wife." He really was bone tired.

"We only did *it* once."

Gideon rolled his eyes. She was going to send him to an early grave. He was sure of it. "We did *it* twice. I assume you were awake this morning. Your eyes were open and you must have woken half the house when you screamed my name as your sweet little... well as you pulsed around me."

"That was morning, not our wedding night."

"It counts. The sun had not risen."

"It had."

"No, it hadn't look, the sun has still not risen. The damned rain has followed us to Cumberland."

"It always rains in Cumberland."

"Not yesterday it did not."

"No."

"Anyway, you said you had a question to ask me once we got into the carriage. Ask it."

"Oh yes. You said you would explain why Lord Byron had to flee to Switzerland. He did something to his wife. What was it?"

Gideon groaned and placed his hands over his eyes.

"My love, it is really not a story that is meant for the ears of a lady."

"You said you would tell me when I was no longer an innocent."

"I did? Was I drunk when I said that?"

"You have never been drunk in my presence, my lord."

"I may have to remedy that," he muttered.

"You are more of a beast than Robert," she cried and punched him on the arm.

"Ouch."

"That's for being a beast and for nipping my arm last night."

He caught her around the waist and plopped her face down over his knee. There was not a lot of room in the carriage but there was enough for his purposes.

"Lady Beattie, you will desist from punching me on the arm. I shall not tolerate it." He was struggling to keep the amusement out of his voice. With his wool coat and shirt on, he had barely felt her fist. Years spent in Gentleman Jackson's Boxing Saloon meant that a punch barely registered with him, never mind one from a female.

"Lord Beattie, what are you doing?"

"Punishing you." He whipped up her skirt. The sight of her white, rounded bottom made his cock start to harden. Damn, he loved every part of her body. He had a horrible suspicion he was beginning to love her. He ran a hand over the rounded cheek then dipped his middle finger between her legs.

Emily gasped and Gideon was now fully erect. He ran his finger through her folds, forward and back, collecting her moisture as he stroked her.

"This is punishment?"

"It is if I do not take you to completion."

"You would not be so cruel, my lord. Please."

"Perhaps. Do you promise not to punch again?"

"I promise."

He ran his finger up to her puckered hole and prodded ever so gently.

"See here?"

"Mm-hmm?"

"This is why Lord Byron is in Switzerland." She looked around and gave him a confused look. "Some gentlemen like to use this entrance instead and Lord Byron obviously did."

"With his wife?"

"Yes."

"And his half-sister?"

"Good God, Emily, I do not know all the man's secrets. His wife told her mother, from what I can make out. No one seems to care that he had relations with his half-sister, just that he buggered his wife."

"That is what it is called?"

"Yes, my love. That is what it is called. Now, will you stop asking questions?" He really had explained far too much, used far too profane language and said much more than he had meant to. He hoped to God she would not repeat it.

"I shall stop asking questions if you use those fingers to give me a release. Otherwise, I shall start asking about Mollies."

Gideon threw his head back on a guffaw as his fingers found her pearl. Then he leaned close. "Yes, my love, Mollies use that entrance too."

Chapter 20

Five days they had been travelling home and Emily could swear the weather was wetter than when they had left. Every night at the inn, a maid would clean her half boots and dry them by the fire and every day they would be soaked by the time she got to the carriage. Gideon had offered to carry her through the mud but that would be so debasing.

The hems of her gowns were all now utterly ruined. She had complained about this to Gideon just the previous night when they had been lying in bed. He had chuckled, kissed her deeply and promised to take her to London and buy her a whole new wardrobe befitting of a viscountess. Emily had sat up, indignant.

"There is nothing wrong with my gowns, except for the ruined hems."

"I did not say there was, but you can wear deeper colours now you are a married lady. The dirt is not as noticeable."

She had not considered it until that moment. Perhaps her odd spillage would also not be so noticeable.

He had been lying watching her, his eyes hooded with lust. "Your mind is working nineteen to the dozen Viscountess Beattie. What are you thinking? I become nervous when you start plotting, you know."

"Nothing of any import."

"I do not believe you." He had caught her and tickled her until she had confessed, then he had declared it a terrible secret and not worth all the fuss. After that, he had positioned her astride him, shown her how to take him inside of her and how to ride them both to release. It had been wonderful. She had been in full control and Gideon had run his hands all over her body, speaking loving words to her until his release was near. Eventually, his words became profanities as he started to thrust up into her. As his body stiffened and she felt his hot release inside her he told her he loved her.

Emily's own release was upon her and she wondered if Gideon knew she had heard his declaration. She had not returned it. She had not known what to say. He had not repeated it. Perhaps he had not meant it.

Now they were trundling on along in a silent carriage, books at their sides, Emily's head resting on his chest and Gideon occasionally pressing tender kisses to the crown of her head.

"Gideon, may I ask a question?"

"Oh God. Not if it's about bloody Byron."

"You have answered all my questions about George Byron, thank you very much."

"George, is it? You are on first name terms with his Lordship, are you?"

"May I ask my question or not, Your Lordship?"

"I am shaking in my Hessians, knowing the sort of questions you ask, my love. I may prefer to face down the whole of Napoleon Bonaparte's forces than have to face another of your questions, but go ahead."

"I wondered if, when a lord and lady were forced to marry due to an indiscretion on the lady's part, after six nights of marriage, it would be truly gauche for the lady to tell the gentleman that she loves him. What do you think?"

He raised an imperious eyebrow at her and a smile tugged at his lips but he looked like he was considering the question when his lips pursed.

"Six nights, eh? Hmm, it would depend entirely if the lady and gentleman had got to know each other beforehand. Say, in a long carriage ride to Scotla... What the devil?"

The carriage was slowing down and there were shouts from outside the carriage.

The door opened and a man with his face covered pointed a pistol through the door.

"Not again," Emily heard herself saying.

"Give me your jewels and money."

Gideon sighed as Emily pushed herself back into her seat. Oh, why did she not ask Aunt Gertrude if she had any more of those fake jewels? Perhaps Gideon had some stored somewhere.

Then the unthinkable happened.

Gideon placed his hand over the end of the pistol and pushed the highwayman backwards as he himself jumped out of the carriage, splashing mud everywhere. Emily scrambled over to that side of the carriage to watch the drama unfold. The young highwayman yelped as Gideon yanked the gun out of his hand and caught him by the throat, shoving him hard against the side of the coach.

"Denholm, get his accomplice. This one looks no more than eleven or twelve. His accomplice can't be more than seven. He's in the trees. I doubt he can carry that pistol any distance, far less shoot the damned thing.

Denholm was already down from the carriage and Emily saw that he was heading toward the boy and John, the stable hand was flanking him on the other side. They were so brave.

"He's just a boy, Gideon," Emily said, as Gideon pulled off the handkerchief hiding the young man's face.

"Old enough to wave pistols in the faces of ladies, aren't you, lad?"

"Please my lord, let my li'l brother go. He's just a nipper. He don't know what he's doing. Hang me but not him."

Hang him! Emily gasped. Would Gideon really have this child hanged?

"What age are you?"

"Thirteen."

"Once I handed you over my jewels, what were you going to do with them?"

"Give them to my stepfather. He'll try to sell them at the market for food."

"And do you think there is a trade for jewels around these parts at present?"

"I'd get more money for a loaf of bread than a diamond, my lord."

"And your stepfather?" There was a sound in the trees and a man on horseback broke through them and into the field beyond, galloping away from him.

The boy closed his eyes. "Guess he didn't want to get hanged too."

"Will you go back to him if I let you go?"

"Don't know where he lives. We walked here for days. Me and ... my brother."

"You do not know where you live?"

"No, my lord. Tis far away though."

The smaller boy was being brought by the scruff of the neck up to Gideon. He had a large bruise on his face, but it was old. It had not been dealt by Denholm or John. That much Emily could tell. The boy's eyes were wide with terror and he was shaking like a leaf on a tree in a stiff breeze.

"And your mother?"

"She died a few months ago in childbed. He got her with child and she died having it. Mrs Jamieson, the vicar's wife said it was her own fault for getting with child before she were wed, but he said it came early. He said it were Jack's fault it came early cause Jack ran away."

Gideon shook his head.

"Who the devil is Jack?"

"I am Jack," said the small boy.

Gideon raised an eyebrow at the little one. "Are you indeed and why did you run away?"

"He were gonna kill me, he said cause I let the pigs out by mistake. I couldn't close the gate. It were too heavy, see." Then the little boy put both hands over his mouth, his eyes wide with terror again.

Oh, this was no good. Emily jumped down from the carriage, splashing even more mud all over the place and Gideon had to throw out a hand to save her from falling. He had loosened his grip on the older boy. It appeared that her husband's aristocratic glare was enough to keep the young man in place.

"And what is your name? Your brother is Jack."

"Gerald, my lord."

Emily crouched down beside the smaller boy and pulled him into a hug. She saw her husband roll his eyes but she cared not.

"It seems, Gerald, that my viscountess has a tender heart. When you are a grown man, you shall understand why it is a good thing to stay on good terms with your wife. When did you last eat?"

"I found some berries this morning, my lord."

Gideon took the boys chin in his hand and lifted it up. "So, I see. The evidence is all over your face, but when did you last eat a meal?"

"A meal?"

"Yes, Gerald. You know, potatoes, stew, oatmeal, something filling."

The boy shook his head. "We've been out here fer days. Mr Bates carn't cook and his mistress, well she's just a lass."

"He has a mistress already."

"I think she's goin' to have his babe. She keeps casting up her accounts in the mornin'. That's what happened to me mother just before she told us she were having his babe."

"Sounds like a grave possibility. So, if I were to tell you to get out of here and go home, what would happen to you?"

The boy shrugged. Gideon looked at Jack then at Emily. Emily caught her husband's gaze and willed him to have mercy on these boys. He could not leave them here in the middle of nowhere to fend for themselves, could he? She knew not to say anything. It had to be his choice. And they had tried to rob them.

"Lady Beattie, that horse looks hungry. Do we have any food in the carriage?"

Emily caught the gleam in Gideon's eye. Perhaps he was as soft-hearted as she.

"I did bring some bread, cheese and a little meat from the inn when we set off, this morning, my lord. Do you think the horse would like that?"

"I believe the horse is a beggar and cannot be fussy, my lady. Denholm, be a good chap and fetch it for us. Is it under the seat, my love?"

"It is."

He nodded to the coachman who moved inside the coach to do his master's bidding. Denholm appeared a few moments later holding a couple of large handkerchiefs filled with bread, cheese and meat as Emily had said. She always brought a little extra food with them in case they got stuck in the mud. Gideon had initially laughed at her for doing it, but he had come to agree that it was a sensible precaution.

Emily expected Gideon to continue to play the game with the boys and tease them, but their eyes were so large with longing when they saw the food, clearly her husband's ire with the children crumbled.

"Go on then. Jack, you take something first, but leave something for your brother."

Jack took a small slice of bread and some cheese and waited for his brother to take an equally small amount of food. Neither boy ate.

"What are you waiting for?" asked Gideon, frowning.

"Are you not eating too?" Gerald asked. "We must wait for the lady."

"I am not hungry. You eat," Emily said. "Please. Eat it all between you." Gideon nodded and shook the food slightly at them. Gerald looked at his brother and shrugged then took a bite, closing his eyes as he did so. Poor little mites.

Gideon handed Gerald the closed handkerchief filled with food. "Go and sit at the side of the road, on the grass with Jack and eat."

"They can't sit there. It's wet," Emily protested.

"We're always wet, my lady. We haven't been dry for weeks. We're fine sitting on the grass."

It was Gideon's turn to shrug and Emily gave a frustrated little sigh.

"Speaking of getting wet, you shall be getting soaking and I do not want you getting a chill. Get back in the carriage."

Emily glared at him. "You don't mind children getting soaked though."

"They are urchins, my love. They are used to it."

"They are babes." He lifted her bodily and placed her inside the carriage then started to force his own way inside. "Oh, you are impossible. What if they were our children, Gideon?"

"Our children would not be attempting to be highwaymen."

"Only because they will have better opportunities in life. That is pure luck, Gideon. One child is born the heir of a viscount, another's mother dies in childbed leaving him with a violent step-father who abandons him. It's so unfair."

Gideon ran his hand through his wet curls. He had left the carriage without a hat. His coat was wet through, his face wet and Emily could tell from the set of his jaw that his temper was frayed.

"No one ever said life was fair, my love." Emily opened her mouth to speak but he raised a finger and she shut her mouth to let him carry on. "We cannot leave them here. They can ride in one of the grain carriages until they dry out and then we shall make sure that Denholm and John look after them in the servants' quarters. I am sure on my vast estate, I can find work for a strong lad and we can put them both into school. Jack can help out in the kitchens until he is old enough. Perhaps he'll be good with horses. Who knows. It is just as well for you that you married a Whig, my love. God knows how many arguments you would have had, were it a Tory whom you had kissed awake that fateful day."

Emily smiled. "I could tell, even as you slept, that you were a kind and honest man."

"You could?"

"Oh yes. You have a lovely face when you sleep."

"And awake?"

"You scowl too much."

"Only when you ask silly questions about exiled poets with questionable proclivities."

"You stopped scowling soon after you explained that."

"My mind was otherwise engaged."

"Yes, it was."

"Stop smiling lasciviously, Lady Beattie, here come the children." Emily bit her lip and wished she did not blush so easily.

"Thank you, my lord," said Gerald. "'Ave, you decided if Jack is goin' ta hang too."

Gideon climbed down from the carriage and told Gerald that neither of them would hang. He offered to take them back to Herefordshire and let them work on his estate, on one condition—that they go to the village school for lessons. Both boys bowed low and promised to behave themselves. Gideon put them in the smaller carriage that transported maize and Emily winced as she heard him threaten to shoot them through the head if they tried to escape. She looked at the pistols lying on their seat. She moved them gingerly and sat down then picked up both weapons.

When Gideon returned he raised both eyebrows and both arms.

"Whatever you want is yours, my lady. Gowns, jewels, gloves, hats, shoes, sexual favours." She laughed as he stepped into the carriage. "I shall even do it like Lord Byron as long as you do not put a lead ball through my chest."

"Write poetry?" she asked, handing him the pistols.

"I would be a terrible poet."

"I have noticed."

He placed the pistols under the seat after having un-cocked them

"Oh yes?"

"Yes. After all, what kind of poet would tell his wife that he loves her as he releases his seed into her body and then would not mention it until they were about to be set upon by highwaymen the next day?"

"The type of poet who loves his wife so much that he wanted her to be able to declare her love for him in her own time without feeling forced into it."

"And if his wife does not feel the same way."

"Then the poet would have to punish his wife for telling untruths because before the children stopped the carriage, the wife had just let it be known that she loved her husband."

"Punishment?" Heat rushed to her core and her nipples hardened at the very thought. Emily glanced down at the falls of Gideon's breeches. He had a veritable bulge there.

Gideon's gaze roved up her body. They had been good since they had left Aelton Manor and kept their sexual activities to the inn bedchambers, but he was like a leashed wild animal now.

"Take off the pelisse, Emily."

She removed it as he undid the falls of his breeches and released his cock into his hand, stroking it slowly as he slid down the squabs slightly until his knees touched the seat in front.

"There," she pronounced sitting primly beside him but licking her lips as she looked at his hard length being expertly manipulated.

"Slide over here and straddle me. You shall need to hitch up your gown."

It was a difficult manoeuvre in a moving carriage but Gideon held her steady as she adjusted her skirts.

"You have done this before," she accused.

He grinned. "No, but I have had seven days on the way to Scotland and five days on the way back to figure out the logistics of how to do it. You do not suppose I was reading all this time, do you, my love?"

"You were working out how to tumble me in the carriage?"

"Y-e-e-es. You disapprove?"

"Not at all. I am disappointed it took you twelve days."

He bit his lip as he tried not to smile. "You are a most impudent wife."

"I believe you like your impudent wife, Lord Beattie."

He held himself with one hand, raised her knee onto the seat beside him and guided her down so that she took him fully inside her. Emily sighed as Gideon groaned, almost feral. He caught her other knee up and guided it onto the seat. All the time, making sure she did not topple. Then he clasped her around the waist and helped her to ride him.

He pulled her face down to his shoulder.

"Correction. I love my impudent wife. Now keep your head low, my love. If you start banging your head on the carriage roof, firstly you will end up with an egg on your skull and secondly, Denholm will know what we are doing."

"I suspect Denholm knows fine what we are doing," she said, working herself up and down his hard length.

"Possibly, but let us not leave him without doubt altogether."

She chuckled and he turned his head and captured her lips.

Emily really did like being married, and she really did love her husband.

Chapter 21

Gideon was actually excited to be bringing his wife home. For a start, he could take her to his comfortable bed and make love to her for hours if he wanted. He would ring for his valet and her maid when he wanted to in the morning and he did not need to worry about anybody judging them or having to load themselves into a carriage.

Of course, he would have to drag his arse out of bed and away from her luscious warm body long enough to arrange the return of Whitsnow's coaches. Also, to decide, along with his steward exactly what he could do with the meagre amount of food he had managed to bring south. The more he had thought on it during the carriage ride home, the more he had become concerned that this really was just a drop in the ocean.

However, it was something. His steward had said the crops had not all failed. There would be something and they had meat.

Getting through the winter would be difficult but it may not be impossible and Whitsnow had promised more food.

The carriage turned onto the long private road up to the manor in the centre of Beattie Park. Emily was practically bouncing in her seat. His hat was still on the seat in front, though Emily had on her bonnet and gloves in readiness to leave the carriage. He bent down to see under her bonnet and moved in to press his lips to hers. She squirmed away.

"Gideon, you will make my face all red and puffy with your day beard."

"I thought you liked my day beard. I thought it was an extra sensation."

Emily bit her lip but placed a hand on his chest.

"You can give me all the sensation you please once I have met the servants."

"You have already met the servants."

"As Lady Emily, a friend of Lady Rutherford. I have not met them as Viscountess Beattie, your wife."

"Is this the same Lady Emily Beresford who was caught in a compromising position, kissing a viscount in his bedroom just over a fortnight ago."

"She no longer exists."

"So-o-o, Lady Beattie does not want her husband's day beard anywhere near her skin from now on. I understand. I shall simply have to bend you over my bed, take you from behind, like a farm animal does, and never kiss you again. It is the only way to fill my nursery."

"Gideon!" She was laughing as she punched him on the arm. He caught her balled fist and gave her a severe look.

"We discussed you punching me, Lady Beattie and your punishment."

Her eyes flared with promised passion but shouts outside the carriage drew Gideon's attention away from his now, obviously aroused, wife.

As they neared the Hall, he could see a crowd of people on the East side of the building—fist raised and shouting. They did not seem happy.

"Stay here," he commanded Emily. He banged on the carriage ceiling and the vehicle began to slow. Before it was fully at a standstill, he opened the door and leapt to the ground, setting off at a run. He looked back to see Emily looking out of the carriage door, but she had made no moves to follow him. He gave her no further thought as he hurried towards the crowd.

"What the devil is going on," he asked the vicar who was standing on the edge of the crowd.

"Oh, Lord Beattie, thank goodness you are here. I've tried to make them see sense but they are not listening to me. Perhaps you shall have better luck."

"What's happening, vicar?"

The man sighed. "Davy Matthews, Eddie Evans and Bill Veitch have been trying to stir up trouble in the village for some weeks now."

"I heard rumblings of trouble before I left for Scotland. I did not know who the main protagonists were though."

"They have been trying to gain others to join their cause, but most in the village are loyal to you.

With the lack of food, my lord, it is becoming a problem."

"Rev Lamb, please, why is everyone at my house?"

"Oh, I apologise, well, Matthews, Evans and Veitch decided you must be home by now so they brought a pistol and decided to come up here, confront you and demand that you do something. I'm not entirely sure what you can do. It's not as if you can turn off the rain, but they found you from home. Instead, they stole food and took it home. They trussed up your poor housekeeper and kitchen staff.

When the villagers found out they marched them back up here en masse to untie your staff. Of course, the rest of your staff had found them and untied them, but now they want justice. They're threatening to shoot them."

"Shoot them?"

"Yes. I know they did wrong, but..."

Gideon held up his hand.

"Allow me."

He started to push through the crowd. As people started to recognise him, he heard his name shouted and whispered around the crowd. When he made it to the front, he found Joseph Andrews, the pub landlord holding a pistol out and pointing it at Eddie Evans.

"Joseph, put the pistol down."

"They trussed up my sister, my lord."

"The vicar told me. They've done a terrible thing. They shall pay for their crime."

"Too right they will. They'll die."

"Joseph, stop it." It was Mrs Barrington the housekeeper and the sister of Joseph. "Put the pistol down. They only had me trussed up for a very short while. The other servants had me untied very quickly after they left."

"Joseph, you do not want to shoot a man in cold blood. You shall hang."

"I won't, my lord. All these fine folks will say I was at the inn serving drinks. No one will be a witness."

Gideon drew in a deep breath. "I shall be a witness and I shall be the one to choose your sentence. If I see you kill a man, I shall have no choice. Besides, would you have all these people swear an oath on the Holy Word of God and tell a falsehood?"

Joseph glanced at him and then back to Eddie. "They would do it. God would surely understand. Who trusses up four women and a young lad to steal food?"

"Someone who is desperate."

"WE'RE ALL DESPERATE, MY LORD!" Gideon stepped back slightly as Joseph bellowed in his ears, but Joseph's resolve was crumbling. Gideon could tell. The pistol was shaking and he glanced uncertainly at his sister who raised praying hands to her lips, pleading with him to listen to reason.

"I make no excuses for what they did, Joseph. They shall pay. Lower the gun."

It seemed as though all the fight left Joseph in that moment. "I'm sorry, Lottie," he whispered in the direction of his sister.

"Bring those men over here."

The men were duly brought to him.

"I am going to sentence each of you to one month in the village prison and...." While he had been speaking there had been noise but there was now a deathly hush. He suspected it was nothing to do with his commanding presence. He looked to his side and his heart dropped into the pit of his belly. Cold gripped him at the sight of Emily held with a filthy arm around her beautiful throat and a pistol pointed directly at her head.

It appeared that the villagers had not tied up Davy Matthews particularly well and he had got free of his bindings. Joseph, in his relief at not being the one to kill other human beings, had let his guard down. Matthews must have taken advantage.

"I want to be let go with food and money. I want a carriage and a couple of horses. All three of us want to go."

"What about your families. You're leaving them here to starve," Gideon asked. He watched Emily closely. Her gaze was determined. Her lower lip trembled slightly but trust was the overwhelming emotion he read in her expression. She trusted him to get her back safely.

Devil take it. He was making this up as he went along.

"I... we... we'll wait until someone gets them from the village."

"That's a terribly long time to wait." *Damn it, think man.*

There was a slight tug on his coat tail and then his hand was pulled behind him and something cold and metallic was placed in it. A pistol. Was that Jack?

Instinct told him he was right, just at the same moment that he saw the scruffy messy brown hair of Gerald behind Emily's shoulder. What the devil was the lad doing?

"Let Lady Emily go or I'll shoot you. She's been nice to me and my brother and if you shoot her, I don't mind 'angin' to get rid of you. Drop the pistol."

Gideon slowly lifted his own pistol and aimed it at Davy. "I won't wait for you to shoot her, I shall just shoot you now. Drop it now or I shoot. Three, two. o..." the pistol dropped to the ground. Gideon dove for the pistol but Gerald kicked it out of the way. The vicar picked it up.

Gideon then grabbed Matthews around the feet and felled him, crawling up his body before planting him a facer with his balled-up fist. His other hand came up to punch the other side of his jaw and Davy grabbed at his face, yowling with pain. Gideon hit again. When he went to land the fourth blow, he was prevented. The smell of lavender surrounded him and she was clinging to his back.

"Gideon, stop! You'll kill him."

"He deserves it," Gideon spat out.

"Maybe so, but you do not deserve to hang, my love."

That pulled him up short. He rocked back on his heels and Emily stood, walking around him and helping him to his feet. She gave Matthews a little prod with the toe of her half boot.

He looked at the man lying supine in the grass. What had he done? He had never lost his temper in such a manner before. Then he turned to find all the villagers watching him, astonishment on their faces.

"Where are the pistols?" There had been three.

"I have them." It was Leishman, his steward. Gideon nodded. At least they were in safe hands. He then turned towards the house, stumbling around the corner at the back of the large mansion only to be stopped by Emily.

"Gideon."

"God dammit, Emily, what is it?"

She did not flinch, nor did she back away when he rounded on her. She lifted her hand and cupped his jaw and smiled oh so sweetly at him. She had seen him behave like a wild animal but still she had a tender smile for him.

"You have to go back and explain your plans for the food and the vicar to hand it out. You explained it to me in the carriage, but I cannot do it."

He waved a hand. "Tell the vicar my plans then and he can explain it."

"No Gideon." He had moved to turn and leave but her tone arrested him. "No. You have to go back and do this. They will only listen to you."

Se gave a mirthless chuckle. "Not after that display of brutality."

"He deserved it."

"I was an animal."

"You were defending your wife. They will all understand that. Gideon, I thought... I th... Gideon, I thought I was going to die." A tear slid down her cheek and she raised a trembling hand to wipe it away. He pulled her into his embrace. "It was my own fault. You told me to stay in the carriage. Even though I was a ninny and disobeyed you, you saved me."

"Actually, Jack and Gerald saved you."

"All three of you saved me. B-b-but you knew he wouldn't go through w-w-w ith it. Thank you."

"Shh. All is well."

"No Gideon." She pulled out of his embrace and swiped at her eyes. "Your people need you. This happened because the food is scarce and they need you to guide them and tell them how you plan to rectify the situation."

Dash it all but she was correct. He needed to do this.

"I have been telling you since I woke up that you are clever and wonderful and I have been proved correct. I love you, Lady Beattie."

With that, he turned back to the crowd at the side of Beattie Hall to explain his plans. The vicar would give out the grain to the needy according to the size of their family and how poor they were. He would also organise for the opportunity for all with excess food to donate it at the church every day. While going through this difficult spell they would work more as a community than they ever had. The Beattie estate would also give all excess food to the church to distribute among the poor. He explained that he would be sending coaches back to Cumberland and asked for volunteers to guard the coaches there and back against highwaymen. He had a few good men willing to give their time.

The three men who had caused today's furore would each serve a month in prison, with Davy Matthews serving two months. They would do hard labour in the fields in that time, working on drainage in the hope that the fields in and around Beattie estate would still manage some kind of harvest. They would be fed and their families would be cared for from the food supplies.

When all questions had been answered and the crowd of people started to head back towards the village, the prisoners in the care of people whom Gideon trusted to be handed over to the prison keeper. Gideon knew they had been given a very light sentence for their misdeeds but he had known these men all his life and it was indeed trying times. He would not think twice about handing down a much harsher sentence if any of them came up against him again for anything more than a drunken brawl.

He turned to find his wife and the two heroes of the hour, Jack and Gerald standing beside Mrs Barrington.

"Well, Mrs Barrington, I understand it has been a trying day."

"It has, my lord, but we have food all prepared."

"Do you now? Well, might I suggest that we find some food for these two young men and beds for them to sleep in? Tomorrow, I intend to take them to the schoolhouse and enrol them, then I should like to find some work for them to do around the estate."

"I can do that, my lord. When would you like dinner served."

He looked at Emily who looked all wide-eyed innocence but there was a gleam in her eye.

"Oh, I think my wife needs a short nap before dinner. Shall we say in two hours?"

"As you wish, my lord."

He was sure he saw mirth in the older woman's features. He supposed they were not fooling anyone.

He drew Emily's hand through his arm and led her around to the front door.

"I believe that while the drama unfolded here in our own version of Drury Lane, the staff were unloading our valises, unpacking our things and preparing our rooms. I think it wise for you to have your nap in my bed, Lady Beattie, do you not?"

"My dear Lord Beattie, I do have the most wonderful memories of your bedchamber. It was where I had my first kiss."

"But alas, my love, you only woke a viscount, not a prince."

"I may not have fallen in love with a prince though. You did not get a princess, just the clumsy, outspoken sister of an earl who asks impertinent questions about Byron."

"You know what happens when you mention Byron, my love."

"Why do you think I mention him?"

They were nearly at his bedchamber. He looked about him but no one was around. He bent and lifted her over his shoulder giving her a swift smack on the bottom as he did so.

"Gideon!" she giggled.

"You really are the naughtiest fairytale princess ever, Lady Beattie," he said as he deposited her on the bed then came down on top of her.

"I think you'll find, my lord, that in this story, I was the prince."

He pulled his head away from her neck which he had started to kiss and looked into her blue eyes which sparkled with merriment. "I suppose you are."

He glanced around his bedchamber where it had all begun. He smiled at the thought that he had a lifetime of mornings when Emily, Lady Beattie would wake him with a kiss.

Epilogue

Gideon did not want to attend this ball and he suspected Emily did not either. The poor thing had been casting up her accounts until early afternoon. Now, however, she was glowing. Possibly a bit too much. Her cheeks were very pink. It was entirely his own fault. Well, he had gone into her room to collect her and the low cut of her gown had taken his breath away. She'd turned, tripped and he'd had to move quickly to stop her crashing into her dressing table.

He'd caught her to him and kissed her. One kiss had turned to two, then three, then he'd pressed kisses to her décolletage and the damned beautiful creature was always trying to get him to tumble her these days. It was worse since she'd missed her courses.

He'd helped her out of her gown so it wouldn't be rumpled but then he'd just let down the fall of his breeches and removed his coat. It had been fast and furious and oh so satisfying.

Now she definitely looked slightly tumbled, at least to him. She was rosy-cheeked and starry-eyed and like the cat who got the cream. Though he felt like the cat who had got the cream. He was going to be a father.

They were standing in the receiving line waiting to be received into the betrothal ball of the illegitimate son of the Duke of Hartsmere to Miss Kathleen Roberts of Connecticut in America. He had only come to town to see his sister. The last thing he wanted to do was celebrate anything with Cedric Onslow. The man was an ass. He was a dandy who wore inexpressibles which made all the ladies uncomfortable, he tried to affect an air of fashionable ennui but just appeared idiotic. Gideon could only feel sorry for the poor chit who would have to suffer marriage to the dolt.

They had arrived at the Duke of Hartsmere in the receiving line. They were announced and Gideon introduced his wife to the Duke and his sister Lady Stanbury. Polite greetings were exchanged and a few words about the ballroom and how lovely the Duke's home was before they moved on to Mr Onslow and his bride. Cedric, with whom Gideon had a passing acquaintance, smiled politely and introduced his fiancée after Gideon had introduced Emily. That was odd. The man was not nearly as sneering or irritating as he normally was. Wearing perfectly respectable silk evening knee breeches and smiling warmly at his betrothed, Gideon could almost believe... but no.

Gabriel had been ill for years and had been kept in the country.

Suddenly the man in front of him became the sneering, arrogant toad whom Gideon knew as Cedric Onslow.

"I should let you meet the rest of your guests. Miss Roberts, it was a pleasure to meet you."

"If you ever need anything, Miss Roberts, please do not hesitate to call on us at Beattie House on Audley Street."

"I shall and thank you."

Gideon steered his wife away.

"She seems lovely," said Emily once they were out of earshot.

"And him?" It was not like Gideon to be judgemental.

She raised an eyebrow. "Was it me, or did he seem to change from perfectly nice to..." she waved her hand. "Arrogant in the middle of our conversation."

"If I did not know better I would believe he was his half-brother Gabriel."

"The Earl of Cindermaine."

"Yes. You know of him?"

She gave him a scathing look. "I am a young lady of the *ton*. I know all the eligible bachelors with titles and money, my lord."

"Hmm, you can stop looking now."

She held her hand over her flat stomach. "Never. We shall have daughters. I must make sure they are married to nice gentlemen."

"Let them at least be conceived and born first, my love."

"Some of the youngest men shall only be thirty-six when our daughter has her come out."

He grimaced. "Stop plotting your children's marriages before we are yet sure if you are increasing."

"Oh, I am sure. When can we go home, Gideon."

He laughed. "Soon."

∞ ∞ ∞

"Can we go yet?" she asked as the waltz music ended.

"Soon."

"You said that hours ago."

"You are very demanding."

"I shall mention that poet again."

"I have stopped reacting to him. There is Stalwood, let us go and speak to him for a moment. Ah, Stalwood."

Myles, Viscount Stalwood who had been friends with both him and Gabriel, the Earl of Cindermaine, at Eton had just led Gabriel's twin from the floor. He looked a little starry-eyed around the young lady. A bit how he felt around his wife.

"Beattie, nice to see you. How goes it?"

"Tough year, old chap. The crops were thin and if it was not for the Earl of Whitsnow and his generosity, I'm not sure we would have made it."

"Yes, Whitsnow is a brooding chap but he is kind at heart."

"Oh, my apologies, Viscount Stalwood, my wife, Lady Beattie. Lady Beattie, Lord Stalwood."

"Lady Beattie." He bowed and she curtseyed.

"I believe we have danced a set or two around the ballrooms of Mayfair, my lord."

"I believe we have too, my lady. A pleasure it has been too."

Emily laughed. "It is kind of you to say so, but I highly doubt it. I know I was named Lady Clumsy."

"Not in my hearing, my lady or I would have slapped a glove in the face of the gentleman who said it."

"You are very charming, I'm sure."

"Nice to see Gabriel is well and standing in for his half-brother," said Gideon.

Stalwood whipped his head towards the man who was supposed to be newly betrothed and then back to Gideon.

"I have no idea what you mean. I hear Gabriel is in the country."

"That man is not Onslow. I have watched him all night. He can affect the air of Onslow for a time then he slips and becomes the friend I knew at Eton."

Stalwood's eyes narrowed and he pursed his lips.

"This is complex. I am not entirely sure what has gone on here but I believe apart from family, you and I are the only ones who know, along with Lady Beattie. I cannot divulge any confidences, Beattie, but please say nothing. Can I ask though, would you be able to get Onslow and me into your club?"

"Onslow?"

"Yes. *That* Onslow."

"Even though you are a Tory, I shall gain you admittance and then I shall convince you of why change is needed."

"I understand why change is needed, Beattie. I just think the Whigs are fools for thinking it's achievable."

"Ye of little faith."

"I shall call on you sometime in the next few days if I may."

"You may," said Beattie. "Now, my wife is tired. I must get her home."

"It was a pleasure to meet you."

Stalwood bowed to them both and took his leave.

"How odd," said Emily.

"Well, the tale of Lord Cindermaine will be a very interesting story. I am intrigued."

The End

About the Author

Em was born and brought up in the Central Belt of Scotland and still lives there. She was told as a child she had an overactive imagination--as if that is a bad thing. She's traded her dreams of owning her own island, just like George in the Famous Five to hoping to meet her own Mr Darcy one day. But her imagination remains the same.

Em's Stalking Links

Facebook Page –
https://www.facebook.com/EmTaylorRomance/
Facebook Group –
https://www.facebook.com/groups/14624948933064
7/
Twitter – https://twitter.com/emtaylor_3
Instagram –
https://www.instagram.com/emtaylor.romance/
Tumblr – https://emtaylorromance.tumblr.com/
Webpage: – http://www.emtaylor.co.uk
Amazon – https://www.amazon.com/Em-
Taylor/e/B00GVEG83M
https://www.amazon.co.uk/Em-
Taylor/e/B00GVEG83M

Other Books by Em Taylor

Regency Series

<u>The Contrary Fairy Tales</u>
Sleeping Lord Beattie
The Cinder Earl's Christmas Deception
Lord Rose Reid and the Lost Lady
Lord Whitsnow and the Seven Orphans -
Coming soon
Lord Greatall's Gingerly Escape – Coming
soon

<u>The Eversley Siblings Series</u>
Saved By a Rake
Restoring Lady Anna
Saved by a Rake/ Restoring Lady Anna
(together)

Individual Regencies

Seven Rogues for Christmas - (Anthology) –
(The St Nicholas Day Wager)
The St Nicholas Day Wager
Lady Harriet's Unusual Reward
A Desperate Wager
A Love Remembered